PURBECK LANDSCAPES

JOHN CHAFFEY

DORSET BOOKS

First published in Great Britain in 2006

Frontispiece photograph: Corfe Castle.

Disclaimer
While the author has walked all the routes described in the book, no responsibility can be accepted for any omissions or errors or for any future changes that may occur in the details given. The author and publisher cannot accept any liability for accident, mishap, or loss arising from the use of this book.

British Library Cataloguing-in-Publication Data
A CIP record for this title is available from the British Library

ISBN 1 871164 57 5
ISBN 978 1 871164 57 2

DORSET BOOKS
Dorset Books is a partnership between
Dorset County Council and Halsgrove

Halsgrove House
Lower Moor Way
Tiverton, Devon EX16 6SS
Tel: 01884 243242
Fax: 01884 243325
email: sales@halsgrove.com
website: www.halsgrove.com

Printed and bound by D'Auria Industrie Grafiche Spa, Italy

Contents

Acknowledgements

My thanks are due to all of those people in Purbeck who have helped me in the writing of this book.
In particular I would like to thank Dennis Smale who read through and commented
on an earlier draft of the manuscript. My extended thanks go my parents
who first brought me to Purbeck on Easter Monday treats in the immediate post-war years.
It was then that I first grew to know and love Purbeck, whose landscape
and scenery has been a constant source of inspiration.
As always I would like to thank my wife Ruth, who has walked the inland
and coastal footpaths of Purbeck with me for over forty years now: her support
and encouragement during the writing of this book have been unfailing.

DEDICATION

To all of my family: Ruth, Helen, David and Sally and granddaughters, Zoë and Sarah

MAP

When reading this book access to Ordnance Survey Outdoor Leisure Map OL15
Purbeck and South Dorset would be useful

Selected Reading

Bruce, Peter, *Inshore Along the Dorset Coast*, Boldre Marine, 1996

Chaffey, John, *An Illustrated Guide to the Dorset and East Devon Coast*, Dorset Books, 2003

Chaffey, John, *The Dorset Landscape*, Dorset Books, 2004

Cooper, Ilay, *Purbeck Revealed*, James Pembroke Publishing, 2004

Davis, Terence, *Wareham, Gateway to Purbeck*, Dorset Publishing Company, 1984

House, Michael, *Geology of the Dorset Coast*, Geologists' Association Guide, 1989

Hyland, Paul, *Isle of Purbeck*, Dovecote Press, 1998

Hyland Paul, *Purbeck, The Ingrained Island*, Gollancz, 1981

Ladle, Lilian, *Explore Corfe Village*, Anglebury Print Partnership, 1988

Legg, Rodney, *Corfe Castle Encyclopaedia*, Dorset Publishing Company, 2000

Legg, Rodney, *Purbeck's Heath*, Dorset Publishing Company, 1987

Legg, Rodney, *Purbeck Island*, Dorset Publishing Company, Revised Edition, 1988

Legg, Rodney, *The Book of Studland*, Halsgrove, 2002

Legg, Rodney, *The Book of Swanage*, Halsgrove, 2001

Lewer, David and Smale, Dennis, *Swanage Past*, Phillimore 1994

Oswald, Arthur, *Country Houses of Dorset*, Dorset Books, 1994

Pitfield, F.P., *Purbeck Parish Churches*, Dorset Publishing Company, 1985

Saville, R.J., *The Village of Corfe Castle*, Dorset County Council, 1994

Saville, R.J., *Kingston*, Dorset County Council, 1999

Saville, R.J., *Langton Matravers*, Dorset County Council, 1995

Saville, R.J., *Worth Matravers*, Dorset County Council, 1993

Treves, Sir Frederick, *Highways and Byways of Dorset*, Macmillan, 1920

Wareham Rediscovered, Amberwood Graphics, Wareham, 1994

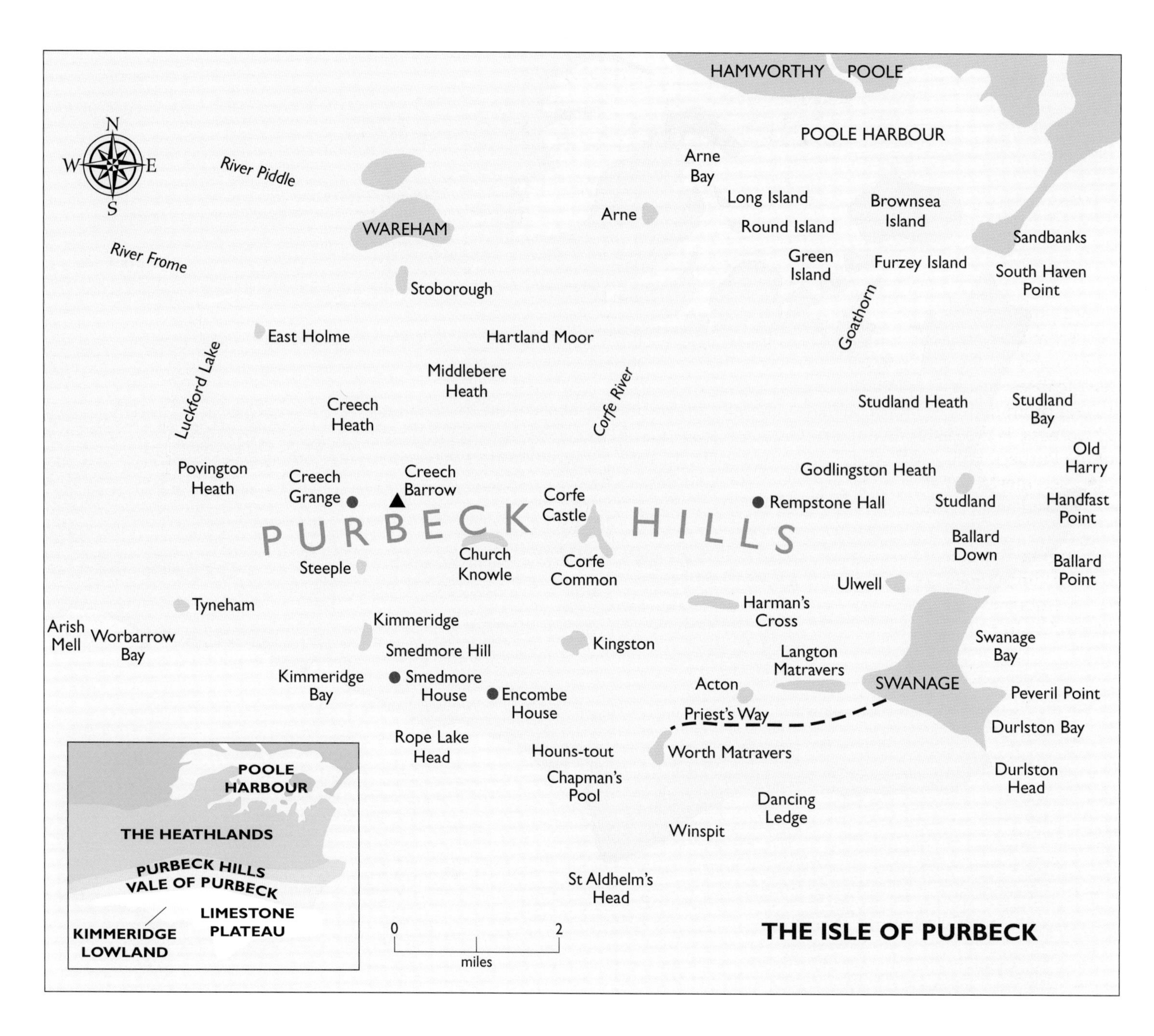
HAMWORTHY
POOLE
POOLE HARBOUR
Arne Bay
Long Island
Brownsea Island
Round Island
Arne
Sandbanks
River Piddle
WAREHAM
Green Island
Furzey Island
South Haven Point
River Frome
Stoborough
Goathorn
East Holme
Hartland Moor
Luckford Lake
Middlebere Heath
Creech Heath
Corfe River
Studland Heath
Studland Bay
Old Harry
Povington Heath
Creech Grange
Creech Barrow
Godlingston Heath
Corfe Castle
Rempstone Hall
Studland
Handfast Point
PURBECK HILLS
Ballard Down
Steeple
Church Knowle
Corfe Common
Ballard Point
Ulwell
Tyneham
Harman's Cross
Arish Mell
Worbarrow Bay
Kimmeridge
Kingston
Swanage Bay
Smedmore Hill
Langton Matravers
Kimmeridge Bay
Smedmore House
Encombe House
Acton
SWANAGE
Peveril Point
Priest's Way
Durlston Bay
Rope Lake Head
Houns-tout
Worth Matravers
Chapman's Pool
Durlston Head
Dancing Ledge
Winspit
St Aldhelm's Head
POOLE HARBOUR
THE HEATHLANDS
PURBECK HILLS
VALE OF PURBECK
LIMESTONE PLATEAU
KIMMERIDGE LOWLAND
0
2
miles
THE ISLE OF PURBECK

Chapter One

The Isle of Purbeck

A Unique Variety of Landscapes

From the damp water meadows of the Frome valley, just to the south of Wareham, much of the landscape to the south appears wooded. Random oak and ash copses intermingle with the more formal outlines of coniferous plantations. Rising prominently from this wooded mantle, beyond the cottages of the little hamlet of Cotness, is the distinctive hill of Creech Barrow, just to the north of the main ridge of the Purbeck Hills. Although not the highest in the area, its summit offers views that embrace most of that special part of south-east Dorset, the Isle of Purbeck, rightly recognised as an Area of Outstanding Natural Beauty.

Creech Barrow from the Frome valley.

Ascending the steep footpath that leads through gorse and heather to the grass-covered limestone capping of Creech Barrow, the panoramic view that unfolds to the north embraces nearly all of east Dorset, with the distant skylines formed by the sweep of the Chalk of the Dorset Downs, Cranborne Chase and the wooded heights of the

Heathland and Poole Harbour from the summit of Creech Barrow.

western New Forest. The green ribbon of the meadows along the Frome, contrasting sharply with the dark coniferous plantations that now cover large tracts of the heathland to the north and south, form a natural boundary to the Isle of Purbeck in the middle distance. The Frome empties into the vast expanse of the salt-marsh-fringed Poole Harbour, with its familiar scatter of wooded islands. The almost uninhabited Purbeck shores of Poole Harbour, seamed with winding creeks, differ markedly from the urban shoreline of Hamworthy and Poole with their ferry terminal, crane-outlined wharves and busy quayside.

The casual eye of the observer on Creech Barrow's summit sweeps beyond Poole Harbour past its two enclosing arms of Sandbanks and the South Haven Peninsula to the open waters of Poole Bay. Sandbanks with its pine-shaded mansions, villas and hotels looks out to empty South Haven with its cover of heathland, oak-birch coppices, and the watery expanses of Little Sea linked to the sea by peaty, bog-myrtle-fringed channels. Southwards, Poole Bay merges imperceptibly with the friendly waters of Swanage Bay, revealed beyond the long stretch of the hog-backed Purbeck Hills. Thus the peninsula of Purbeck is bounded by marine estuary and open sea to the north and to the east. From the summit of Creech Barrow glimpses of the English Channel, which fringes Purbeck to the south, appear beyond the high limestone plateau that forms the southern upland of the peninsula.

Below left: *View from Creech Barrow looking west.*

Below right: *View from Creech Barrow looking east.*

It is the western boundary of Purbeck that has always been the most difficult to define.Tradition has it that the little stream of Luckford Lake, that rises in the shadow of Whiteway Hill in the western Purbeck Hills, and flows north-eastwards to join the Frome near West Holme Manor, marks the western extremity of Purbeck. Inevitably, no trace of this tiny stream can be seen from Creech Barrow. The copses and plantations through which it flows do mark a significant change in the landscape. To the east are some of the largest remnants of Dorset's central heathlands, much scarred by the activities of years of military training, and the great ball clay working at Povington. To the west there is an entirely different landscape. The Chalk ceases to be represented by a narrow ridge of hog-back hills, as in Purbeck, and expands northwards into the open cultivated downland that extends westwards to well beyond Dorchester before swinging north-eastwards to form the great expanse of downland that extends to the Wiltshire border and Cranborne Chase. It is convenient to consider that the coast of the Isle of Purbeck ends at the little bay of Arish Mell, enclosed by the high Chalk cliffs of Cockpit Head and Cow Corner. So the western boundary runs from the coast at Arish Mell inland to East Lulworth and then follows the course of Luckford Lake to the well-developed meanders of the Frome.

Within these more or less natural boundaries, much of the variety of Purbeck can be seen from Creech Barrow's windy summit. The Isle of Purbeck falls quite naturally into five divisions. In the north are the heathlands, part of the great Dorset heath, now sadly so utterly fragmented, which extended from just west of the Avon at Ringwood to Puddletown in the west. At both of these limits of the heath much of it is forested, as it is in Purbeck. To the south of the heathlands are the Purbeck Hills: they run from Handfast Point in the east westwards to Arish Mell, their great billowy sweep only broken by the gaps at Ulwell and Corfe Castle. Beyond, lies the central vale of Purbeck, with its patchwork of copse and pasture, extending from Swanage Bay in the east to wild Worbarrow in the west. This fertile lowland is dominated to the south by the windswept limestone plateau, that meets the Channel in high cliffs that run from Durlston Head to St Aldhelm's Head. Finally, hidden from view from Creech Barrow's summit is the rich cereal-growing lowland around Kimmeridge, which emerges in the shadow of Swyre Head in the east, and extends westwards to the remote Brandy Bay, under the brooding heights of Gad Cliff.

Seen from Creech Barrow, Purbeck's heathland presents a vastly different appearance from the unbroken expanse of heath and pine copse, damp hollows and the occasional valley bottom bog that the casual observer would have experienced in the nineteenth century. Today four main areas of heathland remain: in the west both West Holme and

Povington Heaths lie within the Lulworth Ranges. Alien tracks allow army vehicles free access to the heath, derelict rusting armoured vehicles appear as mournful hulks amidst the reed-fringed pools and windswept heather, and the sudden report of tank gunfire echoes as it is reflected back from the gorse-covered hills to the south. The greatest impact on the landscape of the heath comes not from the military presence, but from the exploitation of the ball clay resources in Povington Pit, the greatest gash in the landscape in the whole of Purbeck.

Povington Pit.

The remaining expanses of heathland in northern Purbeck are all protected as Nature Reserves. Heathland on the Arne Peninsula, which projects into Poole Harbour, is protected within the R.S.P.B.'s Reserve, and includes the remote Arne and Crichton's Heath overlooking the inner waters of the harbour. Hartland Moor and Middlebere Heath form a central National Nature Reserve. In the east Studland and Godlingston Heaths particularly need the protection afforded by designation as a National Nature Reserve because of the enormous tourist pressures from Studland and its crowded beaches. Within these reserves the heathland possesses some of the rarest flora and wild life in southern England.

Hartland Moor.

The observer on Creech Barrow's summit sees woodland covering much of the former heathland of Purbeck. Deciduous woodland occurs as a series of fragmented oak and birch coppices in the area immediately to the north of Creech Barrow. Coniferous woodland, nearly all in the form of public (Forestry Enterprise) and private plantations, has a far greater impact on the landscape, covering great swathes of former heathland both in the west and east. The angular outlines of the plantations introduce an alien geometrical element into the heathland. The dark green plantations of Corsican Pine that occupy much of the former Wytch Heath, Rempstone Heath are not only the dominant theme in this part of northern Purbeck, but also serve to obscure almost completely the surface features of the Wytch Farm oilfield. In particular the huge Gathering Station, with its complex of pipes and towers, is completely hidden from the viewer on Creech Barrow by the dense stands of Corsican pines. The distant Arne Peninsula has acquired a distinctive mantle of conifers which serve to outline its flat-topped profile.

If there is little evidence of Wytch Farm, Britain's largest onshore oilfield, in the landscape as seen from Creech Barrow, the same is not true of the workings of ball clay. The vast open pit of Povington, already noted, lies just to the west of Creech Grange, the elegant country house which lies in the shadow of Great Wood, on the northern flanks of the Purbeck Hills. To the north the relatively new pit at Dorey's Farm scars the copse and pasture landscape south of East Holme, and the tiny workings at

Greenspecks lie half-hidden in the woods at Cotness. Much of the heathland around Furzey Ground has been savaged by former workings of the clay, and today has a somewhat desolate air about it. Old workings can be found throughout the silent copses south of Furzebrook, and the dank overgrown pits, often filled with murky water, have an eerie loneliness not found elsewhere in Purbeck.

Looking west from Creech Barrow a strip of pasture and arable land lies between Great Wood and Creech Grange, adding an element of variety to the rural scene. This narrow band of fertile land runs all the way from Studland in the east to Monastery Farm in the west. Its rich soils contrast markedly with the poor acidic soils of the heathland to the north, and they have encouraged both tillage and pasture, creating an attractive farmscape in the lee of the Purbeck Hills. Sturdy stone farmhouses bring a homely element into the landscape, and small hamlets like East Creech, with its distinctive architecture complete the rural picture.

View from Creech Barrow looking west along Great Wood.

Few of Britain's Chalk landscapes create the immediate impact of the Purbeck Hills. Seen from the distant New Forest heaths to the east of Ringwood, or from the heights of Cranborne Heath east of Shaftesbury, they form a backdrop to the varied Dorset landscape unparalleled in southern England. Their outline becomes clearer when seen across the waters of Poole Bay from Bournemouth. The surging curves of Godlingston Hill and Ailwood Down, and the deep gaps at Ulwell and Corfe create a silhouette in the fading light of a summer's evening that equals, if not surpasses, that of Elgar's beloved Malverns at sunset. From Hengistbury Head, to the east of Bournemouth, distant Creech Barrow appears offset from the crest of the Purbeck Hills, and it is from that familiar viewpoint that the detail of the ridge can be best appreciated. To the west the ridge sweeps away to Arish Mell, its nearby northern slopes mantled by the magnificent indigenous beeches and exotic conifers of Great Wood, one of Purbeck's most treasured assets. Eastwards the hills fall away to Cocknowle, with its deep valley, chalk pit and long abandoned tramway. Beyond, the hills swing away to Corfe Castle, hidden from view, and continue eastwards through Challow Hill, with its television transmitter, to Ailwood Down, with its distinctive Neolithic and Bronze Age barrows. Beyond the gap at Ulwell, the final curves of Ballard Down ease gently down to one of Purbeck's and Dorset's most spectacular coasts. Here the Chalk has been eroded into high cliffs, isolated stacks and pinnacles, natural arches and caves that reveal every weakness in the rock. Seen from any viewpoint, the contrasts between the brilliant white of the cliffs and the blue waters of Swanage and Studland Bay remain one of the most memorable of summer scenes.

The western Purbeck Hills at sunset.

Swanage Railway near Corfe Castle.

The central Vale of Purbeck presents rural Dorset at its most intimate. The urban spread of Swanage in the east stands apart from the remainder of this attractive lowland, whose rurality increases steadily towards the west, culminating in the wild sweep of Worbarrow Bay. In the east, the main road (still known as Valley Road, and dating only from the late 1920s) threads its way through the relatively modern Harman's Cross. The lanes that straggle away from it to the north and south pass between high hedgerows, which obscure a landscape of rich pastures, the now familiar fields of summer maize, and the occasional pond. The northern farms such as Knitson and Ailwood, nestle in the shadow of the Purbeck Hills and command a view across to the damp line of woodlands that extend up the slope to the limestone plateau to the south. Clouds of steam from the trains of the now resurgent Swanage Railway, emitted as their locomotives toil up the bank from Corfe to Afflington, add a new but nostalgic element to this landscape.

Corfe Common adds a welcome wilder element to the countryside south of Corfe Castle. Untouched by cultivation for several hundred years, its gorse and bracken slopes seem to emerge naturally from the surrounding pastures. Its damp hollows preserve rare wetland plants and provide a habitat for uncommon dragonflies. Ancient burial mounds and religious sites crown the ridge. Latterly National Trust policy has been to clear away gorse and bracken, creating a more open landscape in which a wider range of flowering plants can flourish. Beyond the common's farms

Corfe Common.

St Peter's church, Knowle.

such as Blashenwell with its abandoned water wheel, and half-walled duckpond, and Bradle with its elegant chimneys, cluster at the foot of the limestone hills. They look across to the Purbeck Hills and their Greensand-fringed slopes, now empty of settlement apart from the few cottages at Cocknowle. The villages of Church Knowle and Steeple, with their prominent stone churches, and ancient farms such as Whiteway and Barnston Manor, add an important human interest to this fecund landscape.

Beyond Steeple Leaze, the landscape changes and bears some of the marks of military occupation since 1943. Farm buildings still lie ruined, apart from the occasional new barn such as the one at Lutton. Pastures have been invaded by weeds and rushes, and new stone-chip tracks scar the landscape. However, the presence of the Army is seen to have brought some benefits. Valued plants and wild life have a chance to survive that might otherwise have been denied them: Worbarrow Bay has been protected from the worst excesses of the English seaside, and retains its unsullied grandeur, best seen during a winter storm when waves enter its perfect curve after an unbroken run across Weymouth Bay.

The stone landscape of the southern plateau, is in some ways the most distinctive of Purbeck's landscapes. It is, perhaps, the most obvious manifestation of the geology that underpins so much of the variety of Purbeck. Here stone walls replace the thick hedgerows of the Corfe valley, quarry debris reveals stone working around Acton and

The limestone plateau west of Kingston.

Strip lynchets, West Man, Worth Matravers.

along the Worth Road, and stone is the universal building material in houses, and churches, farms and barns. Trees struggle to survive on the windswept expanses of the plateau, and only appear patchily in isolated hollows, in the valleys that run down to Chapman's Pool, and where they have been deliberately planted as around Kingston. Yet this austere landscape has much to commend it. Its three villages, Langton Matravers, with its long sloping main street, Worth Matravers, with its stone cottages clustered around the tree-shaded church and village pond, and Kingston, dominated by its Victorian church, are all special places, the very essence of stone Purbeck. Its well-built stone farmhouses and barns add a sense of strength to the rural landscape. Evidence of past cultivation, embodied in the strip lynchets of West Man and East Man that enclose the Winspit valley, testifies to its long occupation by people. The very openness of the plateau, with distant views of the Channel to the south, creates an impression of a bleak ending to Purbeck's peninsula, reminiscent, perhaps of Cornwall's Penwith.

Kimmeridge village.

The enclosed Encombe valley, and the more open lowland around Kimmeridge provide the final element in Purbeck's varied landscape. Both are floored with Kimmeridge Clay, emerging for the first time beneath the Portland Limestone of St Aldhelm's Head. Encombe, by virtue of its enclosing limestone scarps that reach out to the coast at Houns-tout and sweep round to tumulus-capped Swyre Head in the west, is one of Purbeck's most remote landscapes. South-facing Encombe House itself, reflects brightly the pale winter sunlight when all its surrounding woods are leafless, and Polar Wood, high on the escarpment, earns its name.

Kimmeridge's landscape is altogether more expansive, sweeping up to Smedmore Hill in the east and Tyneham Cap in the west. Within this lowland there are three important human elements that act as focal points in the landscape. Smedmore, like Encombe, is one of the great country houses of Purbeck, and its elegant front looks westwards towards Kimmeridge village, sheltered in a tree-fringed hollow. Kimmeridge is a one-street village, with some of its thatched cottages fronting directly on to the street, whilst others rest, half-hidden behind well-stocked gardens.

The third focus of the Kimmeridge landscape is the bay itself. Here old miners' cottages nestle in the small valley at Gaulter Gap. Fishermen's cottages lie across the bay in the shadow of the ruined Clavell Tower located on the summit of Hen Cliff, made of the same crumbling black shale as the cliffs that extend eastwards to Freshwater Steps. On the cliffs to the west lies Purbeck's first oil well, still productive after nearly forty years. Beyond lies a further reminder of the military presence in Purbeck. Locked and bolted

Kimmeridge Bay.

gates bar entry to the coastal footpath to Worbarrow, open only at weekends, long school holidays and in the summer. Athough sheep and cattle still graze the pastures in the Army's ranges here, buildings such as South Egliston are now only empty shells. Standing and surveying the peaceful Kimmeridge scene, from the quarry at the western end of Smedmore Hill, it is almost impossible to believe that the viewpoint is scarcely 20 miles from a conurbation of half a million people in Bournemouth and Poole.

The variety of landscapes in Purbeck owes much to the underlying rocks, although it would be an oversimplification to say that geology was the sole reason for the remarkable changes in scenery that occur within 60 or so square miles of south-east Dorset. Purbeck is underlain by rocks of the Mesozoic and Cainozoic Eras of geological time. These strata are arranged in east-west outcrops, the result of erosion of a huge upfold in the rocks, the Purbeck monocline, that was produced by earth movements some twenty million years ago.

The southern part of Purbeck is underlain by Jurassic rocks. The oldest of these strata is the Kimmeridge Clay, composed of dark grey shales with intervening harder bands of limestone, known as cementstones, which form the Kimmeridge Ledges running out to sea from the cliffs on either side of Kimmeridge. Since the Kimmeridge Clay is relatively easily eroded by rain and rivers, its outcrop forms a landscape of smooth gentle slopes that extend for some miles either side of Kimmeridge village.

The south coast of Purbeck near Dancing Ledge.

Worbarrow Bay.

The remainder of southern Purbeck is limestone country. The Portland Limestone forms the inland escarpment that runs from Tyneham Cap to Smedmore Hill that bounds the Kimmeridge lowland on its inner margins, and then outcrops along the coast from St Aldhelm's Head to Durlston Head. Resting on the Portland Limestone are the Purbeck Beds mostly Cretaceous in age, that outcrop over much of the plateau to the west of Swanage. Important building stones, the freestones, occur within the Purbeck Beds, although they are separated by thinner bands of shale and marls. The Purbeck Marble, in reality a shelly limestone composed of the remains of freshwater snails, outcrops in a belt at the foot of the slopes leading up to the limestone plateau from Purbeck's central lowland. This outcrop is pock-marked with ancient quarries from which Purbeck Marble was obtained.

Cretaceous rocks also underlie both the central vale of Purbeck and the Purbeck Hills. Unlike the Jurassic rocks in the south of Purbeck, which only dip gently to the south, the Cretaceous rocks show much steeper dips to the north. The Wealden Beds, a set of variegated sands, shales and clays, outcrop in vivid colours in Worbarrow Bay and in Swanage Bay. These rocks are easily eroded by the sea, hence the two bays at either end of their outcrop in Purbeck. They offer little resistance to erosion by rain and rivers and thus form a lower-lying area than the harder limestones to the south and the Chalk to the north. Where harder bands of sandstone outcrop in the Wealden Vale, higher upstanding ridges, such as Corfe Common, occur. The pastoral character of the central vale owes much to the fertile soils that develop on the Wealden Beds.

Just to the south of the Purbeck Hills, the Greensand outcrops to form some of the best soils in Purbeck, that are much devoted to cereal growing. The Chalk that forms the

Purbeck Hills differs from that found in the great sweep of the Dorset Downs in the north of the county. In Purbeck it has been thrust into a near vertical position by the earth movements of twenty million years ago. These movements have also been responsible for changing the Chalk here into a much harder and more brittle rock than elsewhere in Dorset. The Chalk is therefore a resistant rock, forming the high hog-back hills that extend across Purbeck from east to west, and the high cliffs at either end of its outcrop in the peninsula. Soils of the Chalk are often thin and flinty, but fields of arable land still appear on the crest of the hills.

Immediately to the north of the Purbeck Hills, the oldest of the Tertiary rocks occur. The Reading Beds and the London Clay occur as narrow east-west strips, and their fertile soils are responsible for that belt of cereal and pasture land between the hills and the heathland to the north. Purbeck's heathland is underlain by sands, clays and gravels, belonging to the Poole Formation. Generally the sands and clays give rise to thin acid soils that only yield well if heavily fertilised. These soils therefore support heathland, or the coniferous plantations that have replaced it. The clay occurs as irregular lens-shaped bodies, which have been widely worked for their commercial value. So geology is fundamentally responsible for the five principal divisions of Purbeck, by virtue of the east-west orientation of the different rock groups, and their varying resistance to erosion. Geology contributes to the landscape in other ways too. Soil variations across the different outcrops provide farmers with different opportunities.

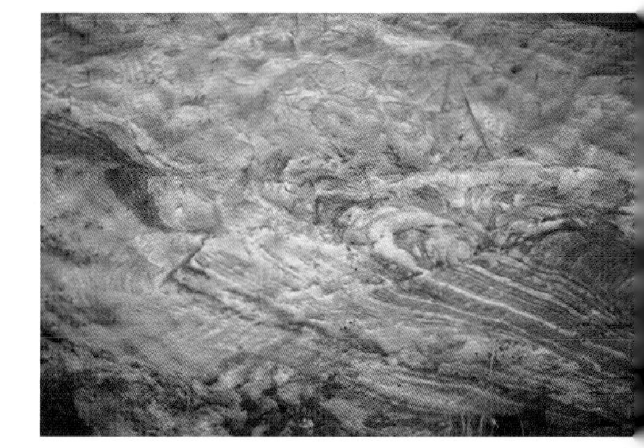

Rocks of the Broadstone Sand, Poole Formation, south of Redend Point.

Mineral resources within the rocks have produced their own distinct quarrying landscapes in the limestone in the south of Purbeck, in the claypits of the heathland, in the mostly abandoned Chalk pits within the Purbeck Hills and in the one brickpit that remains on the Wealden Beds near Ulwell. Different rocks mean availability of different building stones. Although Portland and Purbeck Stone are used throughout Purbeck, they make their greatest contribution to the village and farm landscape in the south. Bricks from the Wealden Clay appear in both farms and villages in the vale. Flint from the Chalk is seldom used decoratively in buildings near the rock's outcrop, since, like the Chalk, it was so crushed and fractured in the earth movements of twenty million years ago. In the north, heathstone, a tough, indurated brown sandstone, is used widely in both farms and cottages.

Although less important than geology, other factors contribute to the unique variety of Purbeck's landscapes. Aspect and exposure of the landscape in the peninsula have created some remarkable differences between the south coast, the windswept stone plateau, the open crest of the Purbeck Hills and the more sheltered lands in the central

Gnarled hawthorn, Godlingston Hill.

Hill Bottom.

lowland, and those in the lee of the hills. The open landscape of the limestone plateau, with the occasional sturdy barn taking advantage of a small sheltered hollow bear perhaps some resemblance to the windswept limestone uplands of north-west Yorkshire, although the latter are much higher, and face much harsher winters. Such a landscape is replaced within a mile or so by the central Vale of Purbeck, where copse and thicket cluster thickly. Here trees form an important element in the landscape between Swanage and Harman's Cross, particularly in the damp ill-drained hollows where the Swanage Brook draws together its tributaries. Perhaps more surprisingly, the shelter afforded by the reverse slopes of Gad Cliff have encouraged the development of Tyneham Great Wood, still shrouding the memories of one of Purbeck's great houses.

From Flower's Barrow to Ballard Down and Handfast Point the landscape is almost treeless: here and there a gnarled and bent hawthorn is testimony to the strength of the winds that race across Weymouth Bay and along the ridge of the Purbeck Hills. Yet in their shadow are some of Purbeck's finest woods. In the west, Great Wood and its westerly continuation form a splendid backdrop to the Creech estate. Woodland extends almost unbroken on the north slope of the Purbeck Hills from near Rollington Farm eastwards to Kingswood overlooking Godlingston Heath. The heathlands to the north are hardly sheltered, particularly when a bitter winter easterly blows uninterrupted across Poole Bay. Nevertheless dark green conifers, tough and unyielding, mask much of the original cover of heath and bog.

Finally, remoteness brings its own character to the hidden corners of Purbeck, distinguishing them from the parts that are relatively accessible. Arne and Steeple, at opposite ends of Purbeck, have seen little change in the present century, largely because they are tucked away in remote parts of the peninsula. By way of contrast, both Stoborough, at the end of the Causeway south from Wareham, and Harman's Cross, on its ridgetop between Corfe and Swanage, have grown substantially. If one hamlet owes its delightful character to remoteness, it must surely be Hill Bottom, nestling in its deep valley that runs from Swanworth to Chapman's Pool.

Purbeck is perhaps a microcosm of lowland Britain. Its heathlands recall the landscapes of the New Forest and the Surrey heaths. The Purbeck Hills, a Chalk landscape, here have echoes of the Surrey Hogsback and the downlands of south-east England. The central vale of Purbeck has affinities with the clay vales that sweep across the southern Midlands and lap around the central sandstone ridges of the Weald. Purbeck's limestone lands hint at similar landscapes in the Cotwolds, the limestone lands of the East Midlands and the open country of Lincolnshire's limestones.

Chapter Two

The Coast of Purbeck

The coast of Purbeck offers some of the peninsula's finest, and best-known landscapes: most of it is part of the World Heritage Site designated in 2001. It is a coastline of marked contrasts, stemming from the different aspects that emerge along Purbeck's changing shores. Along the north is the estuarine or the Poole Harbour shoreline, with its sheltered and unruffled waters. After South Haven Point there is the dune-fringed coastline that runs southwards to Redend Point at Studland. Another small bay follows with the crumbling cliffs of South Beach, Studland. Here Chalk makes its appearance and grows in splendour and majesty as it begins to dominate towards Old Harry, Handfast Point and Ballard Point. Swanage Bay is twentieth-century seaside Purbeck, with only fleeting glimpses of the original cliffs once Shep's Hollow has been passed.

Old Harry and Handfast Point.

Peveril Point marks the beginning of an altogether different coast. Although Durlston Bay, like Swanage Bay to the north, faces east, its exposure and rocky, boulder-strewn foreshore give it a sense of emerging grandeur and wilder cliff architecture. Beyond Durlston Head, the vertical cliffs of Portland Limestone that extend all the way to St Aldhelm's Head create a formidable rampart against south-westerly gales that blow up the Channel. From St Aldhelm's Head the great spectacle of the southern coast appears in the massive, landslide-threatened cliffs of Emmett Hill and Houns-tout. Here Kimmeridge Clay appears at their base, and dominates all the way, with vertical and disintegrating shale cliffs, to distant Brandy Bay, lurking in the shadow of Gad Cliff. The western extremities of Purbeck's coast offer some of its most intense variety, with the ancient landslides under Gad giving way to the bastion of Worbarrow Tout. Beyond are the pastel shades of the unstable Wealden cliffs of Worbarrow itself, succeeded in their turn by more landslides under majestic Flower's Barrow. Finally, precipitous Chalk appears again in the oddly named Cow Corner, and eases down gently to the delightful stream-eroded gap at Arish Mell. Beyond, the Chalk soars up to the great white heights of Cockpit Head and its stunning and frightening rock falls, the beginning of the powerful and world-famous Lulworth coastline.

Portland Limestone cliffs, south coast of Purbeck

The northern shores, facing out across the expanse of Poole Harbour, are quiet, unfrequented and not well known. Today this heath and pine-fringed shore is almost empty, and largely inaccessible from the landward side. It is a much indented coastline, with creeks ('deeps' or 'lakes' in local water lore) fingering up into the low plateaux of heath and woodland. It still bears traces of a busy industrial past, with the old clay-shipping wharf at Ridge, the pier at Goathorn where other clay tramways terminated, and Ower Quay, at one time important in the Purbeck Marble industry. Ridge Wharf is today an important yachting centre on the reed-fringed estuary of the Frome, but in the past it was one of the busiest of the outlets for the ball clay that was being produced in the heathlands to the south. The original tramway from the large claypit to the south of Furzebrook House was built in 1840 by the Pike brothers straight across the heath to the tiny hamlet of Ridge. At first it terminated at a short canal but was later extended to the Frome itself. Sailing barges took the clay from Ridge down to Poole for onward shipment, although they were later replaced by a steam tug, the *Frome,* built and launched at Ridge, which towed barges down to Poole. The system of tramways linked to Ridge for exporting clay survived for over 100 years, with the last remnant of the network closing in the mid 1950s.

Russel Quay.

About 800 metres (half a mile) to the east of Swineham Point, where the Frome empties its waters into the vast expanses of Poole Harbour after its long journey from Evershot, another abandoned clay shipment site is seen at Hyde's Quay. It was from this quay that the clay worked at the Purbeck quarries of Thomas Hyde was shipped across Poole Harbour by barge, and then onwards to the Mersey, and eventually to the Staffordshire Potteries of Josiah Wedgwood. His quarries closed in the late eighteenth century, and little remains to show of their original existence. About a mile to the north-east, Russel Quay is another site, now long abandoned, from which clay was shipped to Poole: it also saw the import of coal, which was used throughout the Arne Peninsula and elsewhere in Purbeck. Just beyond Russel Quay is a telling reminder of the long term survival of the clay industry: Arne Pit, hidden by huge bunds along the southern shore of Poole Harbour is one of the three remaining opencast clay pits in Purbeck, the others being at Povington in west Purbeck, and at Dorey's Farm just south of Stoborough. Gold Point, a little further on was once the Purbeck terminus of a busy ferry to the Hamworthy Peninsula. Arne Bay has the largest expanse of *Spartina* marsh in Purbeck, and was a source of the export of plants and seeds of *Spartina* to other parts of the United Kingdom and abroad.

Shipstal Point, south of Arne Bay.

To the south, Middlebere Lake and Wych Lake, extend their watery arms deep into the heathland, and are now almost silted up. Just to the north-east of Middlebere Farm, a quay on Middlebere Lake was used for the shipment of clay from the pits worked by Benjamin Fayle. It was first used in 1806, and barges took the clay to Poole where their cargo was transferred to larger vessels for the trip to the Mersey.

Silting of the channel meant that this shipment point had to be abandoned in the mid nineteenth century, and it was replaced by the new deep water port at Goathorn, much farther down the north coast of Purbeck. Wych Lake , also had its clayport, and a ferry to Poole. Ower Bay, which penetrates much less deeply into the heathland, also has its important links with the past. Although there are only remnants of a decaying landing stage at Ower, it was important at a much earlier stage than the other ports farther west along Purbeck's north shore. It was essentially a port for the export of stone from the quarries much farther to the south in Purbeck. Huge quantities of Purbeck stone and Purbeck Marble were brought across the heath to Ower. Here flat bottomed barges were loaded with the stone and it was then taken out into South Deep where it was transferred to larger vessels for export to many parts of southern England, and beyond in Europe. This busy trade appears to have ceased by the time Hutchins was writing his county history in the nineteenth century – 'Ower seems to have been formerly the chief port of the Isle of Purbeck, and it was the principal, if not the only, quay for the exportation of stone and marble.' Today, a few blocks of stone on the edge of the bay are the only reminders of the former trade. The trade was also remembered by the practice of kicking a football from Corfe across the heath to Ower, where a pound of pepper was paid to the occupants of Ower Farm as a form of toll for the allowed transit of the stone to Ower Quay.

The two major inlets to the east of Ower Bay, Newton Bay and Brands Bay are now largely silted up and occupied by *Spartina* salt marsh. Between these two bays is the Goathorn

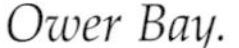

Ower Bay.

Goathorn Pier.

Peninsula, with its pier reaching out into the waters of South Deep. This pier was to become the most important point for the export of ball clay after the ports higher up along the south shore of Poole Harbour gradually became silted up. It seems that the clay pits at Newton, first worked in the 1860s, were linked by tramway to the pier at Goathorn. With the gradual silting up of the Middlebere outlet for the Norden pits near Corfe Castle, it was decided to build a new railway some 5 miles long to link up with the Newton line to Goathorn. It opened in 1905, and the new pier on the deep waters of South Deep became a major outlet for the clay pits of the Purbeck heathland. It operated for over thirty years, but the Goathorn railway closed in 1937 with the working out of the Newton clay pits. Interestingly, the Goathorn line was also used for the transport of stone from the Purbeck quarries for the building of the Training Bank which stretches out from Pilot Point at the southern end of Shell Bay. It was built in the period 1924–1928 to encourage tidal scour at the entrance to Poole Harbour, and thus maintain an adequate depth of water in the main channel used by shipping to and from the harbour. Although Goathorn's pier remains, the busy sound of clay wagons being emptied into waiting vessels has long since gone. Goathorn today resounds to the persistent hum of British Petroleum's oil rig engaged in outreach drilling under Poole Bay in order to exploit the more distant reserves of the Wytch Farm oilfield.

Brands Bay on the western side of the South Haven Peninsula.

So Purbeck's northern shoreline, today a quiet and serene coastal landscape of low cliffs and deeply penetrating, mud-lined creeks, has not always been bereft of man's activities. Even in Domesday times there was evidence of salt pan operation along its sheltered shores, and for a thousand years after that its little ports, wharves and quays were important outlets for Purbeck's mineral resources. Little remains today of this busy industrial past, apart from the ruins of piers and quays and some fragments of stone to remind us of its value to Purbeck as an important transit point for the export of its minerals.

The southern enclosing arm of Poole Harbour is the South Haven Peninsula underlain in the west by the sands of the Poole Formation, and in the east by much more recent sand dune deposits. The boundary between the two areas of the peninsula is an old sea cliff that runs from Studland north-westwards along the inner shores of Little Sea. This inland body of water was first shown on a map published in 1721, where it was shown as a tidal inlet with an opening eastwards into Studland Bay, and partly enclosed by an early dune ridge. Successive maps show that Little Sea gradually became isolated from the open sea: by 1886 the Ordnance Survey 25 Inch map shows that it was almost cut off. The smaller body of water known as Eastern Lake appears to have been formed between 1894 and 1900.

The growth of sand dunes has occurred steadily over the last few centuries. Captain Cyril Diver, in his classic study of 1933, recognised three main ridges, with the oldest one, known as Third Ridge, being the farthest inland. The whole system of ridges narrows towards the south, and the Inner Ridge here is the equivalent of the Second Ridge farther to the north. Since Diver's survey there has been a steady growth of the coast towards the east, and a new ridge, known as Zero Ridge has been formed. From time to time small embryonic dunes form in front of Zero Ridge, but rarely seem to survive long enough to warrant a new designation such as Zero-zero Ridge. At the present time there is considerable erosion of the dunes in the southern end of Studland Bay, at the southernmost end of Knoll Beach and on Middle Beach. Although attempts have been made in the past to protect the dunes against this erosion, current policy is one of strategic retreat, and the dunes are retreating towards the west at what some would regard as an alarming rate. The source of the sand for the continued build-up of the South Haven Peninsula seawards has always been something of a mystery. Current opinion is that it is from the seabed beyond the entrance to Poole Harbour, where there are a considerable number of sandbanks such as Hook Sand. Sand from the erosion of cliffs in Poole Bay would have found its way to Hook Sand and then across the Swash Channel (the deep water entrance channel to Poole Harbour) to Studland Bay.

Studland Dunes are now managed by Natural England (formerly English Nature) as part of the Studland Heath National Nature Reserve. They display quite remarkable vegetation changes from the seaward dunes inland (a process known as ecological succession). After the initial colonisation of the dunes by sand couch grass and sea lyme-grass, marram grass, with its dense mat of roots firmly fixes the dunes in place. Over a period of time other species, such as sand sedge, hawkbit and sea bindweed begin to colonise the landward side of the new dunes and form a denser mat of vegetation. Zero Ridge is now firmly fixed in position by these successive colonisations. Heather is now beginning to appear on the landward side of Zero Ridge, having already invaded the ridges to the west. Gorse has also invaded these ridges extensively to the extent that the soils now have a much higher organic content than those to the seaward – hence the older dunes are often referred to as grey dunes, compared to the coastal yellow dunes, where organic content is much lower. Between the dune ridges are the slacks, where moisture-loving plants, such as cross-leaved heather, creeping willow and even the insectivorous sundew appear. Thickets of alder and birch appear in Zero Slack behind Zero Ridge, and Scots Pine also makes a perhaps unwelcome appearance. Farther inland the damper slacks are occupied by birch-sallow carr, and oak-birch scrub appears in the drier areas. Management of the dune complex now involves pine-cutting to prevent the spread of Scots Pine and also

Studland sand dunes.

cutting the birch-sallow carr to encourage the growth of other aquatic plants. With thousands of visitors on the Studland beaches on a fine summer's day, management of the whole dune complex has become a huge task for the National Trust, responsible for the whole of the Nature Reserve. Balancing the need to preserve a fragile ecological system, and the provision of adequate visitor facilities is central to successful management. Considerable areas of the dunes are now designated for restoration, and trails and nature walks are designed to encourage the visitor to understand the delicate nature of the dune ecosystem. Both Knoll Beach and Middle Beach have information services, shops and cafés and behind Knoll Beach is the ecologically friendly Study Centre. The most serious current concern of National Trust management is the continuing erosion at southern Knoll Beach and Middle Beach. A policy of strategic retreat, which involves the re-siting of threatened beach huts farther in land and the abandonment of the seaward side of the dunes to erosion by the sea, is now in place.

Redend Point.

Beyond the dunes to the south is Redend Point, cut in the Redend Sandstone (now renamed as the Broadstone Sand). Clays in the upper part of the cliff on the side facing north, yield some very interesting plant fossils, and lignite fragments dating from some 50 million years ago. Small caves have been cut by the action of the sea, and at low tide the slippery wave-cut platform eroded by the sea appears. Within the sandstones at Redend Point there are vertical pipes of the iron oxide limonite: they appear to have been formed by the oxidation of original pyrite pipes of uncertain origin.

South Beach, Studland.

Surmounting Redend Point is Fort Henry. This was built by Canadian engineers during the war in 1943 to enable high-ranking officers and even royalty to watch the practice landings for D-Day that were taking place on the Studland Beaches to the north. Cleaned up and tidied, it is now an important heritage site along this coast. Studland's South Beach is backed by low cliffs cut in the oldest sands and clays of the Poole Formation and, farther south, in the London Clay. In the southern corner of South Beach is one of the most important sites in Dorset's geology. Here the Chalk, that forms so much of the splendid scenery of the Dorset coast, makes its first appearance. It emerges from beneath a cover of the oldest Tertiary rocks, the sands and clays of the Reading Beds (now known as the West Park Farm Member). It first appears at beach level and then rises progressively higher in the cliff towards Old Harry Rocks and Handfast Point. The junction between the Chalk and the younger beds above is called an unconformity, and is marked by a layer of rolled flints resting on the Chalk. The plane of the unconformity represents the long period of geological time during which the Chalk was uplifted, and eroded before the lowest beds of the Reading Beds were laid down on top. Close by there are

Junction between Chalk and Tertiaries, South Beach, Studland.

The Pinnacles.

several examples of pipes, vertical tube-like features that penetrate down from the Tertiary Beds into the Chalk. Solution within the Chalk has opened up vertical lines of weakness forming the pipes: debris from the overlying Tertiary Beds has been washed down into the fissures. Farther east the Chalk forms increasingly high cliffs in Wood Cove as Old Harry is approached. Narrow promontories enclosing small bays that are gradually being widened occur along this section of the coast: they are the result of the sea eroding along joints, lines of weakness in the Chalk.

The whole cliff complex at Handfast Point or the Foreland is one of the most dramatic in the Isle of Purbeck. Here the Chalk is almost horizontal and exposed sufficiently to be under almost constant wave attack. Marine erosion has worked along lines of weakness in the Chalk, the joints and bedding planes, to produce a series of caves and natural arches. In the case of the latter, caves have been driven in from either side of small headlands until they meet, forming an arch. Eventually the arch will collapse, leaving a stack separated from the main cliff. Old Harry is the classic example of such a stack. Originally Old Harry was accompanied by Old Harry's Wife, but the latter succumbed to marine erosion in 1896. Erosion at the base of Old Harry will ensure that it will suffer a similar fate in the future. The much larger island of the Foreland or No Man's Land was attached to the mainland in the relatively recent past – it is said that in 1770 a man could creep along a relatively narrow and precipitous path to Old Harry. The area of the former connection of the Foreland to the mainland is now known as St. Lucas' Leap. It acquired its name as a result of a greyhound of that name leaping over the cliff whilst hare-coursing and being killed on the rocks below. Old Harry is said to be a mediaeval name for the Devil, and today the area of short chalk turf opposite No Man's Land is known as Old Nick's Ground. At one time there was a large cave, Parson's Barn, below Old Nick's Ground but it has since collapsed in 1963.

Southwards from Old Nick's Ground two further stacks appear just offshore from the high Chalk cliffs. These are known as the Pinnacles – the northern one is known as Little Pinnacle or Haystack, and its companion is simply known as Pinnacle. Both were formed in a similar way to Old Harry and his Wife, but have a different profile simply because of a harder Chalk base to the stacks. It is said that a pair of peregrine falcons nested in a hole at the top of the Pinnacle at the turn of the nineteenth century. Beyond the Pinnacles the vertical Chalk cliffs display one of the outstanding geological structures along the coast of the Isle of Purbeck – the Ballard Down fault.

This is a curved fracture in the Chalk: to the south of it the Chalk shows almost vertical bedding; to the north the dip of the Chalk reflects the curve of the fault and begins to

Shep's Hollow and damaged groynes, 2001.

lessen almost immediately and becomes increasingly less steep to the north, so that by the time Handfast Point is reached, it is almost horizontal. Many attempts have been made to explain this unusual structural feature in the Chalk but there does not appear to be a universally accepted solution to the problem that the fault presents.

Westwards from Ballard Point the Chalk continues to present almost vertical cliffs. Just before Punfield Cove is reached, geological conditions change and the cliffs become susceptible to landslides. The appearance of the Gault Clay in the base of the cliffs renders the whole of the Chalk above unstable. The most notable recent landslide occurred here in January 2001. A huge section of the cliff slipped along a curved fault plane, disrupting almost all of the cliff-face and disturbing the beach at its foot to the extent that the beach was visibly uplifted and the Gault Clay thrust upwards to form a small ridge on the seaward side of the pebbles that make up the beach. The whole cliff has remained unstable, with further rockfalls above the landslide.

Punfield Cove.

From Punfield Cove southwards stretches the long curve of Swanage Bay, extending all of the way to Peveril Point and its dangerous tidal race. Beyond Punfield Cove where the Lower Greensand cliffs are now much overgrown, the bay is cut everywhere in the sands, and clays of the Wealden Beds. The strata are particularly unstable, prone to landslides and easily eroded by the sea. A measure of the amount of erosion is easily seen just to the south of Shep's Hollow, where groynes built in the twentieth century have now had their inner roots eroded away and remain as forlorn broken structures serving no useful purpose: these groynes have now been replaced. Nevertheless the reds, oranges and browns of the Wealden Beds bestow an attractive and colourful background to the waters of Swanage Bay. South of Shep's Hollow the unstable nature of the Wealden Beds is a constant threat to the promenade, beach huts and even the cliff top villas and hotels. It is a threat to which there is no obvious answer, and highlights the problems presented by building too close to an unstable cliff margin.

Swanage has been rightly proud of the amenity of its sandy beach, which has been one of its outstanding assets as a seaside resort. The beach has always remained more or less stable, enclosed by the two protecting arms of Ballard Point and Peveril Point.

In *The Hand of Ethelberta,* Hardy wrote of Knollsea as a 'seaside village lying snug within two headlands as between a finger and a thumb.' When the flood defence scheme was completed in the 1990s, the outlet for flood waters was built as a small jetty in the centre of the bay. This structure was to alter dramatically the stability of the beach. In the past, beach material was allowed to drift from south to north around the bay. The flood scheme outlet acted as a huge groyne, and prevented beach material moving northwards, with the consequence that there is now a significant accumulation of beach material to the south of the jetty, with a consequent starving of the beach to the north, where the level of the beach has fallen alarmingly in recent years. Solutions will be needed, and include the building of further groynes and beach nourishment, now completed (2006). The latter has been seen as a necessary remedy to retain Bournemouth's beaches in recent years, and may become essential at Swanage. One can only ponder the contrast between the desperate need to manage the beach and cliffs at Swanage with the situation at Worbarrow, where a similar beach backed by Wealden Beds occurs. Here in a wilder and almost primeval environment beach processes operate unhindered to create some of Purbeck's most stunning coastal scenery. The remainder of Purbeck's north-south coast extends from Peveril Point – the 'sinister ledge of limestone, like a crocodile's teeth' to much sturdier Durlston Head.

Between the two promontories is Durlston Bay, with its crumbling cliffs, that display a section of the Purbeck Beds which is the type section for geologists – a standard exposure of these beds against which similar exposures elsewhere are compared.

The Purbeck Beds in Durlston Bay are particularly important for their record of mammal evolution at the beginning of Cretaceous times. Samuel Beckles made his valuable excavations at a quarry in the Purbeck Beds close to the bay in 1857, after

William Brodie had found a mammal jaw on the shore of Durlston. Beckles' collection of mammalian remains is now housed in the Natural History Museum in London. Landslides in Durlston Bay are an ever present threat to the blocks of apartments built on the cliff-top in the twentieth century. Although an expensive coastal defence scheme (some regard it as an unacceptable eyesore) may have removed the immediate danger in the centre of the bay, landslides still occur, with the most recent occurring in the wet winter of 2000-2001, which threatened gardens on the cliff-top and which also necessitated the closure of the coastal footpath for essential repairs.

High on the cliffs of Durlston Head is the splendid Victorian castle, built by George Burt and completed in 1888. It is the principal remnant of Burt's attempt to develop the area as a high class residential district in the mid-nineteenth century. Its main use has been as a restaurant: in 1905 Treves described it as 'a stronghold of the Bank Holiday period, in which are combined the features of a refreshment buffet, a tram terminus and a Norman Keep'. Today it is managed as part of Durlston Country Park by Dorset County Council. In 2003 the lease of the castle was purchased by the South West Regional Development Agency, and it is intended that it should become a key visitor centre for the Dorset and East Devon World Heritage Site. Within the grounds of the castle, one of the most enduring monuments is the Great Globe, weighing forty tons. The country park covers nearly 260 acres and is managed in a sensitive way so that the different environments of the area, which include both the coastal cliffs and the inland areas of limestone downland, can be explored and enjoyed by a public educated and informed by the excellent visitor centre.

West of Durlston Head the coastal landscape takes on an entirely different aspect. The coast as far west as St Aldhelm's Head is a slope-and-wall feature, with the gentle upper slopes formed of Purbeck Beds, often with a cover of periglacial material, succeeded seawards by Portland Limestone forming exposed vertical cliffs. In the limestone there are a number of well-marked faults, and occasionally they bring the more easily eroded Portland Sand up into the base of the cliff. Where the Portland Sand is attacked by erosion, overhangs develop. These wave-lashed cliffs are broken only by small steep-sided valleys that create a ready environment for the working of the limestone for building purposes. The first small valley occurs at Anvil Point, almost in the shadow of Durlston Castle, and to the west the Seacombe and Winspit valleys provided the opportunity for quarry workings in the nineteenth and early twentieth centuries. Apart from the quarries this wild and desolate coastline has never been the site of long-lasting human occupation, and has been the site of shipwreck and maritime disaster in the past.

To the west of Durlston Castle the first old quarry working on the cliffs is encountered. Tilly Whim Caves are old galleries driven into the cliffs to work Portland Stone. The origin of the name 'Tilly Whim' is interesting: 'whim' is local dialect for timber derrick, or perhaps winch; 'tilly' refers to a quarryman called 'Tilly'. The earliest reference to stone working here is in 1703, and the quarries yielded steadily throughout the eighteenth century, but demand in the early nineteenth century fell off and the workings closed in 1820. The 'caves' then became a tourist attraction, which remained open until the late twentieth century, when they became increasingly unsafe, and were closed.

Anvil Point lighthouse.

On the far side of the deeply incised valley is one of the great landmarks of the Purbeck coast – the Anvil Point lighthouse. It was built in 1881, partly as a response to three particularly bad shipwrecks on this coast in the short space of two years (1878–1879), and was opened by Joseph Chamberlain, then President of the Board of Trade. It has a powerful beam visible for 24 miles, flashing every ten seconds. In common with most other lighthouses it is now fully automatic, and, and its sparkling whitewashed buildings are now used for holiday accommodation.

Dancing Ledge.

Between Anvil Point and Dancing Ledge the cliff landscape of this limestone coast displays a remarkable series of caves. Most of them are simply responses to differential erosion by the sea. Where faulting occurs in the Portland Limestone, the lines of weakness are exploited by the sea, and caves such as the well-known Blacker's Hole have developed. It was said at one time that there was room for three fishing boats alongside in Blacker's Hole, but roof falls have made this no longer possible. After Green Point, (its name stemming from the algae deposited by the small stream that drains over the cliff from time to time) is Dancing Ledge, reached by a path that winds down from Spyway Barn and Langton Matravers. Various origins have been suggested for its name. First recorded in 1811, the name may reflect waves 'dancing' on the flat lower ledge. Alternatively, it was suggested that the ledge was as large, and as flat as a dance floor. Perhaps, most plausibly, it might be the 'dark spring ledge', referring to the spring from which water issues to spill over Green Point to the east. There are two ledges here: the upper one, which has been the site of intensive quarrying of the Portland Stone, and the lower one from which the quarried stone was taken out to waiting ships offshore. Quarrying has long since ceased on the upper ledge, although the galleries where the Bottom Freestone was worked still remain. They are now sealed by metal grills, with holes left to allow access by their bat population. The lower part of Dancing Ledge is cut in the so called Cherty series of the Portland Limestone, named after the black nodules of siliceous chert that are found in the beds. The lower ledge itself is formed by the so-called Prickle Bed or Puffin Ledge, named after the puffins that used to nest immediately above the ledge. It is from the lower ledge that flat-bottomed boats, usually rowed by two men, took their loads of stone to larger vessels waiting offshore. The ruts worn by the horn carts that delivered the stone to the boats can still be seen, as well as recesses for the loading gibbets and a hole for anchoring berthing lines. The swimming pool in the lower ledge was blasted by quarrymen for the use of the pupils of Thomas Pellat, the headmaster of Durnford Preparatory School, who owned the land at Dancing Ledge.

More quarries are found along the cliff-top between Dancing Ledge and the Seacombe valley. Before the Hedbury quarries are Platters, Scratch Arse and Topmast, the names of which have a generally dubious origin. Hedbury quarry is in two parts: the larger, East Hedbury, is sometimes known as 'Cannon Cove' with its old gun pointing seawards, now raised on a plinth by the Langton Preservation Society in the mid 1970s. The cannon may have come from the wreck of the *Halsewell,* or it may be the sole survivor of batteries established along the coast after the French invasion scare of 1803. Beyond is Mike Bower's Quarry, with the famous Pig and Whistle Cave to the west – a small blowhole, which hisses and whistles with advancing waves on stormy days.

Two steeply incised valleys meet to reach the southern coast of Purbeck at Seacombe – the ' valley opening on to the sea'. In wet winters the water table in the limestone rises sufficiently high to nourish small streams in the bottom of both of the Seacombe valleys, and often they will flow until well into the spring months. At the mouth of the valley thick alluvial deposits, with much angular material, suggest that the valleys were much deepened during the Ice Age, when meltwater from the snowfields over southern Purbeck would have coursed down towards the sea. The opening in the cliffs formed by the Seacombe valley proved to be an ideal site for the working of the Under Freestone of the Portland Limestone series. Today, the galleries which were last actively worked in the 1930s, stand empty and silent, the home of important bat colonies. Just beyond Seacombe is the site of the wreck of the East Indiaman, the *Halsewell* on the 6 January 1786. Anchored offshore to ride out a severe storm, the *Halsewell* drifted on to the rocks and broke up remarkably quickly. Some crew managed to escape by clambering up the rigging on to the cliff face, but only 82 out of the 250 on board survived.

Winspit, which may be derived from 'a stone pit with a winch', is the largest of the old quarry complexes along this southern coast of Purbeck. It once again benefits from the gap in the line of Portland Limestone cliffs cut by the Winspit streams. In common

Winspit quarries.

with the Seacombe streams the valleys are deeply incised, with an inner valley being cut within a broader and more open outer valley. The geology is slightly different here, since it is farther towards the west, and the upper or Pond Freestone is exposed in the upper parts of the valley walls. Both freestones were worked here, and galleries at ground level mark the workings of the Bottom Freestone, and the suspended openings high on the quarry wall mark the position of the working of the Pond Freestone. The working of dimension stone for the building industry continued much later at Winspit, and the quarries finally closed after the Second World War. Today they have a forlorn air about them, with ruined workshops and other quarry buildings open to the sky and echoing to the incessant crash of the waves on the rocks below. The Winspit valley displays the remarkable remains of a once prosperous mediaeval farming landscape. Strip lynchets, a form of terracing, which enabled the steep valley slopes of West Man and East Man to be cultivated, give the Winspit valley a distinctive appearance. The construction of the strips was a response to increased population pressure in the countryside. The lynchets have survived sufficiently well to be respected when the same slopes are cultivated today, so a form of strip cultivation still survives.

The height of the cliffs begins to rise steadily towards St Aldhelm's Head. Kimmeridge Clay eventually appears at the base of the cliffs, and above the Portland Sand is seen underlying the Portland Limestone. On the summit of St Aldhelm's Head, there are many reminders of its importance as an operational site for the Telecommunications Research Establishment during the Second World War. The ruins of Chain Home Low Radar Station are first encountered, tucked into a quarry terrace from much earlier stone-working activity. Another hut housed scientists working on early radar research. A monument to the work of the radar research scientists stands beside the coastal Path. It depicts in skeletal parabolas the shape of aerials designed by Sir Bernard Lovell to transmit and receive radar signals of very short wavelength. Slightly inland from the National Coastwatch Lookout is the eleventh century St Aldhelm's Chapel. Although distinctively Norman, later buttresses have strengthened it: a roof cross dates from 1873. Legends concerning the chapel abound, and Worth Fair saw a 2-mile procession from the village to a flower-bedecked chapel. It saw use as a coastguard store briefly, but today it stands, dank and empty, the scene of the occasional church service. High on its lofty stone plateau, it is one of the enduring monuments along the South West Coast Path.

From the high viewpoint of St Aldhelm's Head, the varied cliff profiles of western Purbeck can be seen, from the nearby sullen masses of Emmetts Hill and Houns-tout to the distant Gad Cliff and the rockfall-gashed Chalk cliffs east of Lulworth. Here the

Houns-tout and Chapman's Pool.

coastal geology is laid bare for all to see, and wonder at the amazing variety of the coastal landscape. Nearby Emmetts Hill carries a capping of Portland Limestone above the Portland Sand and the landslide-obscured Kimmeridge Clay. Beyond the half-visible Chapman's Pool is the dark and menacing mass of Houns-tout. Kimmeridge Clay forms the coast from Freshwater Steps' waterfall as far as distant, but unseen Brandy Bay. Swyre Head, Purbeck's highest land, sits back from the coast carrying its distinctive tumulus and broods on the landslide remnants below its summit. Distantly, the threatened Clavell Tower looms above Kimmeridge Bay, and beyond, Tyneham Cap marks the end of Kimmeridge's delightful lowland.

Between St Aldhelm's Head and Emmetts Hill is the steep-sided Pier Bottom – a dry valley that hangs above the boulder-strewn beach below. Active landslides extend from the bottom of the valley down to the beach, but in the past this does appear to be another point from which stone was shipped out from the nearest quarries – hence the name Pier Bottom. Today there is little evidence of the existence of the pier, although blocks of dressed stone can be found on the beach. Just to one side of the shallow head of the valley is St Aldhelm's Quarry, the only active working in the immediate area. Emmetts Hill is one of the most dramatic cliffs on the southern coast of Purbeck: its capping of Portland Limestone has been weathered out into castellated forms, with the joints in the limestone opened up into deep and penetrating 'gulls', which have aided rock falls here. Screes of the limestone lead down to the old landslides which extend down to beach level. Most of these landslides are now overgrown, suggesting that they may not have been active since Pleistocene times (the Ice Age).

Half way along Emmetts Hill is the splendid Royal Marines memorial, looking out across the entrance to Chapman's Pool to the great mass of Houns-tout on the far side. Chapman's Pool is one of the most distinctive embayments of Purbeck's coastal landscape. It is cut in the relatively unresistant Kimmeridge Clay, which forms crumbling cliffs prone to landsliding, particularly at the western end in the shadow of Houns-tout. Boulder arcs mark the position of former landslides on either side of its entrance, but the most recent is at the western end marking the landslide of winter 2000–2001. Two small streams drain down to Chapman's Pool, one trickling down from West Hill Bottom, and the other coming down from Hill Bottom. Both are deeply incised into the Kimmeridge Clay, with miniature landslides giving their sides a very broken nature. In the second half of the nineteenth century, Chapman's Pool boasted a lifeboat station, and has been the haunt of fishermen for much longer. Today fishing for lobsters, crabs and prawns is still carried on from the few buildings clustered around the stone slipway nestling below the heights of Emmetts Hill. Most days the range safety vessel for the Lulworth Ranges moors in Chapman's Pool, to monitor the prohibited area of sea offshore from the Gunnery shoots.

From any angle along the coast Houns-tout appears as one of the most shapely, and sinister of all of Purbeck's southern cliffs. Much of its lower part is occupied by old landslides, although activity is still pronounced at the eastern and western ends. The lower part of Houns-tout's cliff, with its impenetrable thickets of blackthorn and boggy hollows, is known as Molly's Garden. Higher up is the Cherry Garden or Half Cliff, immediately beneath the cliffs of Portland Sand, with their disintegrating capping of Portland Limestone. The second Earl of Eldon was responsible for the construction of the dramatic road to Encombe House that traversed across the face of Houns-tout to follow the course of the lake in the Encombe valley up to the house. Cuttings had to be made on either side of Houns-tout to enable the route to make the crossing beneath Half Cliff. Both are still readily visible today, particularly the one on Houns-tout's eastern flank. Landslides wreaked havoc with this panoramic approach to Encombe and it was eventually replaced by the present road down from Kingston through Quarry Wood. The Coastal Footpath steeply descends Houns-tout's western flank, past the seldom visited Egmont Bight to the seaward end of South Gwyle, where the little stream finally falls over Freshwater Steps on to the shale platform below. The ruins of an old pump house lie just above the waterfall: sea water was pumped from here up to Encombe House where it fed salt water into Lord Eldon's bath.

From Freshwater to Brandy Bay beyond Kimmeridge, the cliffs are formed of Kimmeridge Clay. Dry shale crumbles readily, and a constant hail of shale fragments is

Clavell Tower.

encountered along the foot of these cliffs. The dip of the Kimmeridge Clay is everywhere to the south-east, and is well picked out by the hard bands of greyish white cementstone that stiffen up the thinner beds of shale, including the famous Basalt Stone Band and the White Stone Band. These cementstones form the notorious Kimmeridge Ledges offshore and they were the site of one of the most tragic of Purbeck shipwrecks in January 1920, when the *Treveal* foundered on their treacherous rocks. After abandoning ship, only seven of the 43 on board survived the hazardous passage to Chapman's Pool. The Blackstone Band is sufficiently bituminous for it to have been the basis of much of the past industrial activity in and around Kimmeridge Bay. A chance igniting in the early 1970s near Clavell's Hard, caused it to burn in the cliff for several years. The remains of old tramway lines at the top of the cliff to the east of Kimmeridge are another reminder of the past exploitation of the Blackstone shale in this area. The last important landmark of this coast before Kimmeridge is Clavell Tower, built by the Revd John Clavell in 1830. It was rarely used by his family, and then became a lookout for coastguards for much of the nineteenth century. Threatened by the rapid recession of the cliff it is now owned by the Landmark Trust, who have raised sufficient funds for it to be moved a short distance inland, where it can be used as holiday accommodation.

Kimmeridge Bay is cut in the dark shales of the Kimmeridge Clay, but much of the character of the bay, particularly at low tide, is derived from the cementstone bands that form the ledges that run out to sea from the shaly shores. Probably the most important of these ledges is the Flats Stone Band, which forms the platforms along the western side of the bay, and also Broad Bench, which separates Kimmeridge Bay from Hobarrow Bay to the west. The Washing Ledge Stone Band appears high in the cliffs on the western side of the bay, and descends to form the ledges just to the west of Gaulter Gap where the little stream, running in an incised valley, empties into the bay. On the eastern side of the bay the Maple Ledge Band forms another prominent ledge: here the other small stream that drains into the bay slips over the cliff to form a small waterfall. Close by is the headquarters of the unique Purbeck Marine Wildlife Reserve with its aquaria, and facilities for guided tours. The reserve has its own underwater camera and an underwater nature trail in the bay for divers.

Oil well, Kimmeridge.

The exploitation of the Blackstone resource in the past resulted in much industrial activity around the shores of Kimmeridge Bay. In prehistoric times, the shale was used for bangles found on the skeletons of Iron Age inhabitants of the area. Roman times saw its use for a whole range of household articles. An alum works was established on the bay by William Clavell in 1600, and he extended his interests to salt-boiling and glass manufacture, but none of these activities met with real commercial success.

Brandy Bay.

There are still traces of the pier and dock that he built in the seventeenth century, and his glassmaking plant on the site was intensively excavated in the late 1980s. The nineteenth century saw much more activity based on the Blackstone, but none of it was enduringly successful, although the remains of a pier to the seaward of the seventeenth century one still survive. Distillation of the shale produced naphtha, pitch, greases, fertiliser and paraffin wax. Briefly, gas refined from the bituminous shale was used to light the streets of Paris. The Kimmeridge Oil and Carbon Company worked the shale in the 1880s, and a cement-making industry operated briefly in the 1900s. Perhaps the best surviving remnant of nineteenth-century industry is the row of miners' cottages built in the 1860s at Gaulter Gap. Modern industry is represented by the oil well on the cliffs on the western side of the bay. Oil was discovered here in 1959 in a reservoir in the Cornbrash at a depth of over 550 metres (1800 feet). Production has continued beyond expectations, and road tankers still take the oil to the BP depot at Furzebrook. Beyond the cliff-top oil well, the territory of the Lulworth Ranges is entered, and access to the bays to the west is limited to weekends and holiday periods. After the somewhat sinisterly-named Charnel, the ledges of Broad Bench, slowly disintegrating on their western side, lead into Hobarrow Bay. At its western end the Flats Stone Band, displaced by faulting, forms the ledges known as Long Ebb, which eventually lead to Brandy Bay, with its inevitable overtones of smuggling. Here several cementstone bands descend to sea level and the Blackstone makes its re-appearance. Brandy Bay is, however dominated by the great rock bastions of Gad Cliff.

The western end of Gad Cliff.

Gad Cliff, so named after the resemblance of its angular profile to the wedges used by Purbeck quarrymen, is one of the most spectacular features of the Purbeck Coast. Its distinctive wall of vertical cliffs of Portland Limestone can be seen from many different points of vantage on the south Dorset coast between Portland Bill and St Aldhelm's Head. Beneath the Portland Limestone is the greyish outcrop of the Portland Sand, which overlies the Kimmeridge Clay. This juxtaposition of rocks, where permeable limestones overlie impermeable rocks below is a classic landslide situation. The slopes below the Portland Beds here are mostly old landslide features, although considerable sections are now more or less stabilised. This lonely undercliff, reputedly the home of an unthreatened adder population, is also the haunt of a flock of feral goats that some say were introduced by the army some twenty-five years ago.

Huge boulder fields exist where fragments of Portland Limestone have been brought down by landslides from the cliffs: Wagon Rock is the largest boulder at the foot of the landslides and effectively divides Brandy Bay from the stretch of water to the west known as Wagon Bay. Gad Cliff ends almost abruptly at the small embayment of Pondfield Cove, with its rocky boulder-strewn shores. It separates Gad Cliff from the great mass of Worbarrow Tout to the west, and the gap between the two may represent an ancient exit of the Tyneham gwyle stream to the south, or, alternatively, it may mark the line of passage of a small tributary of the Tyneham stream flowing in from the south. Worbarrow Tout, with its wooden targets a somewhat alien feature, is partly Portland Beds (on the seaward side) and partly Purbeck Beds, on the flank facing Worbarrow Bay. Here is one of the finest sections of the Purbeck Beds, stacked layer-on-layer, complete with dinosaur tracks.

It would be no overstatement to say that Worbarrow Bay is one of the finest of the coastal landscapes of southern England. Treves found it 'a bold, virile sweep of coast… not only the most beautiful on the Dorset shore, but one of the most picturesque in England'. On its southern side it is bounded by the shapely mass of Worbarrow Tout, all green turf overlying steep grey cliffs. Much more dramatic cliffs form its northern boundary: here the Chalk, constantly eaten into by fresh landslides, forms a great white wall that extends westwards to Cow Corner. Between is the well nigh perfect curve of Worbarrow's shingle shore, built ridge-upon-ridge by waves surging across Weymouth Bay. Great Chalk and Greensand boulders brought by landslides, festoon the northern limits of the Bay, whilst patches of golden sand around the mouth of the Tyneham stream echo to the cries of busy holiday children in the summer. In the centre of the Bay, the shingle ridges are the haunt of lonely fishermen on winter's grey and listless days. Behind the beach are the land-slide-prone cliffs formed of the Wealden Beds, now only just over half the thickness they

Worbarrow Bay, with derelict cottages.

display at Swanage Bay. Treves eloquently described them as 'lower cliffs, radiant with colour, for they are streaked with yellow, with carmine, with Pompeian red, with the tint of rust, with the brown of dead leaves.'

Silent on summer evenings after the holiday visitors have left, and home only to wheeling gulls when the great waves of winter crash on the dark shingle, Worbarrow now carries no population on its wild and lonely shore. For generations, a busy and sturdy fishing community once lived here, catching lobsters and crabs that Celia Fiennes found 'very large and sweet'. The Miller family was the nucleus of the folk who lived on the Worbarrow shore, and they found additional excitement in being involved in the smuggling that was rife in the nineteenth century. They survived as a Worbarrow family until the forced evacuation of 1943, when they were said to be 'really heartbroken' at having to leave their homes. Worbarrow also had its coastguard station, which closed in 1912. Holiday houses appeared at Worbarrow in the early twentieth century, but they too, like the fishermen's cottages, ended up as ruins, initially with roofs open to the sky, but eventually just piles of stones marking the position of the walls. So Worbarrow today has an eerie air about it, reminiscent of other Army ranges such as Castlemartin in Pembrokeshire, or more distantly of abandoned crofts around Sutherland's lonely lochs.

Overlooking Worbarrow Bay from the north, is the great Iron Age hill fort of Flower's Barrow on Ring's Hill. In the early Iron Age it was probably a single enclosure with

Arish Mell and Worbarrow Bay.

surrounding bank and ditch, but a second defensive ring was added in the late Iron Age. On the southern side these defences have been eroded by landslides falling down to the northern shores of Worbarrow Bay. Within the ramparts there are small depressions marking the position of houses, together with storage pits, and a quarry from which material to build the ramparts would have been taken. There are splendid and breath-taking views from Flower's Barrow in almost every direction, but the most spectacular is that looking south-westwards to Arish Mell and beyond to the cliffs of Cockpit Head and the shores of distant Mupe Bay.

Descending the steep western slopes of Ring's Hill towards Arish Mell, the unusual dry valley of Halcombe Vale can be seen towards the coast. This valley has been truncated at either end by coastal erosion, and 'hangs' over the cliffs in both places. It was here that Churchill reviewed troops and the tanks that bore his name in April 1942. Arish Mell is the western limit of Purbeck's coast. Treves saw it from the high road running to the south of Lulworth Castle. He describes it as 'a bewitching dip in the coast… where is a rounded beach and a spring of ice cold water. Seen from the high road, the gap appears as a triangle of blue sea with its base in the clouds and its point in a green dell… When a white sail is crossing the azure gap the picture of this embrasure in the hills is complete.' Arish Mell – 'the mill near a topographical feature resembling a buttock' – is still a dramatic cleft in the Chalk ridge running from Rings Hill to Bindon Hill above Lulworth., but it has undoubtedly lost some of its charm since the days when Treves could describe its beauty so aptly. It is now the site for the outflow from the former Atomic Energy Research Establishment at Winfrith: access to the beach is forbidden. Treves' ice cold spring is now a weed-infested trickle, surrounded to the north by rusting hulks of armoured vehicles no longer required since the demise of the Cold War. The sad little stream bears little witness to the power of its predecessor that eroded deeply to cut the gap between the ridge to the east and west. However, Purbeck's coast ends here in a scene where the brilliant white cliffs of Cockpit Head, ever-threatened by new rockfalls, look across the blue waters of Arish Mell's neatly carved inlet to the less extravagant cliffs of Cow Corner – still one of Dorset's coastal treasures.

Chapter Three

The Heathlands

'To recline on a stump of thorn in the central valley of Egdon, between afternoon and night, as now, where the eye could reach nothing of the world outside the summits and shoulders of the heathland which filled the whole circumference of its glance, and to know that everything around and underneath had been from prehistoric times as unaltered as the stars overhead... The great inviolate place had an ancient permanence which the sea cannot claim. ...The sea changed, the fields changed, the rivers, the villages and the people changed, yet Egdon remained.'

(Thomas Hardy, *The Return of the Native*)

'The Great Heath, when surveyed as a whole, is a haphazard tract of sand covered with heather, bracken and gorse, presenting highlands and lowlands, bald hills and dry, corroded glens... The tone of the moor is a russet-brown, splashed by bracken with green and by the heather with purple. Under the summer sun marvellous colours appear, which break, as the clouds ride over, into infinite modulations. A far-away plateau may be Gobelin blue, and a nearby hillock bronze-brown. There may be here a bare slope of mushroom-coloured sand, and there a reedy marsh of parrot-green'

(Frederick Treves, *Highways and Byways in Dorset*)

Both Thomas Hardy, in the nineteenth century, and Frederick Treves, in the early twentieth century, admirably captured much of the awe-inspiring presence of Egdon Heath. Treves entitled the relevant chapter in his book 'The Great Heath' and at the time of his writing, the sombre and desolate heathlands had probably not changed much from the same uninhabited and mysterious expanses that Hardy was describing forty years earlier. This was Dorset's own essential wilderness, smaller, but possessing the same frighteningly lonely character as Rannoch Moor in the Highlands or the unrelenting and unyielding wastes of Sutherland, long since deprived of their population. Treves describes the Great Heath as stretching from 'Poole in the east to within sight of Dorchester in the west... while towards the sea it extends to Winfrith and joins the heathland of the Isle of Purbeck.' So Purbeck's heathlands were essentially an adjunct of the Egdon Heath of Thomas Hardy or the Great Heath of Treves.

Godlingston Heath.

Egdon suffered grievously during the course of the twentieth century. Great expanses of coniferous plantations spread across the heath to the north and west of Wareham, and over much of the ridge between the Frome and Piddle rivers to the south-east of Puddletown, and to the south of Tolpuddle. Bovington Camp remorselessly sucked in heathland for training of armoured vehicles, even if its wide open spaces were not entirely lost as they were with the relentless march of the conifers across the lonely expanses of heath. After the Second World War the Atomic Energy Authority appropriated another huge slice of heathland for its Winfrith Research Centre. On the eastern margins of the Great Heath, the ever increasing demand for homes for the population of the Bournemouth-Poole conurbation saw housing estates encroaching on the domain of heather and pine. Patches of heath only remain to the north of Wareham on either side of the road to Sherford Bridge and Morden: around Bovington tanks still rumble over despoiled heath between the Camp and Turner's Puddle.

Middlebere Heath, looking south to Corfe Castle.

Heathland has been lost in Purbeck too, but not to the same extent. Purbeck's open spaces originally extended from just east of East Lulworth village to the sea at Studland, southwards towards the Purbeck Hills and northwards to the shores of Poole Harbour and the water meadows of the River Frome. Military training requirements mean that much of the heathland to the west of the road from Stoborough to Steeple is now in the hands of the Ministry of Defence. Ball clay workings still scar the heathland that remains between the Steeple road and the main road across the heath to Corfe Castle and Swanage. Huge tracts of coniferous woodland now exist between the valley of the Corfe River and the old ball clay workings at Newton. Despite all of these losses, heathland still remains within the Lulworth Ranges, albeit damaged by decades of shell fire and tank manoeuvring: the habitat is still more or less intact. In the east Stoborough Heath, Hartland Moor and Studland Heath are National Nature Reserves, where heathland is protected for all time. Much of the remaining heathland has protection afforded through it being designated a Site of Special Scientific Interest.

Creech Heath.

Much of the landscape of the heathlands is open rolling country based on the sands, clays and grits of the Poole Formation, with cappings of river gravel as in the Arne Peninsula. Most of the valleys are shallow and are often peat-filled. After the post glacial transgression, the short rivers flowing into Poole Harbour began to silt up and peat accumulation in the valley bottoms followed. The most interesting single landscape features are the Agglestone and the Puckstone just to the west of Studland. The name Agglestone seems to be derived from *aetheling* and *stan* meaning' Prince's Stone'. Legend has it that the Devil threw it at Corfe Castle, but his aim failed him and it fell several miles short. The Agglestone was at one time a pedestal rock crowning a knoll rising between two marshy valleys. However, in 1970 it appears to have collapsed to its present tilted position, the result of the immediately underlying strata gradually being eroded away. Dr Hardy, writing in 1910, described the way in which the Agglestone was eroding, both through frost action and rainwash, and forecast its eventual collapse. The Agglestone itself is made of iron-cemented sandstone, known locally as the Agglestone Grit. It is described by some authors as being not unlike Dartmoor tors, although the latter are of course formed of granite. The Agglestone has more in common with some of the isolated rocky outcrops on the Millstone Grit in West Yorkshire such as Brimham Rocks. It is an unusual remnant of erosion by rain and rivers : the slopes leading up to the rock are full of very coarse sandy debris not unlike the 'growan' found around the Dartmoor tors, which is mostly residual sandy quartz debris.

The Agglestone.

The Puckstone (derivation *puca* and *stan* – 'goblin's stone') is a very much smaller feature altogether, only about four feet high and crowning a small knoll about 800 metres (half a mile) to the west of the Agglestone. It has a number of bare outcrops of sandstone on the slopes leading up to it, and in this respect is perhaps more like a typical Dartmoor tor. Until recently the knoll was covered with gorse and it was obscured, but this has now been cleared, and the Puckstone is now visible from some distance around.

The Puckstone, with Agglestone in background.

Most of the paths around the Agglestone and the Puckstone are littered with grit debris. This material, which is extremely durable, is known as 'heathstone' and has been widely used locally in buildings. One writer has suggested that the Agglestone is only a remnant that has survived quarrying in the immediate area. The quarrymen worked the stone for doorsteps, walling stones and hand millstones.

The heathland landscape of today is not an entirely natural one. When the first hunter gatherers moved into the area in about 8000BC much of the land to the north of the Chalk ridge in Purbeck would have carried a cover of dense woodland, including pine, oak and hazel, elm and birch. They may have temporarily cleared patches of woodland but it was not until the early Bronze age that settlers began to move down from their preferred territory on the Chalk ridge to the lower lands nearer Poole Harbour, once their own lands had become degraded. Clearance of the woodland led to gradual changes in the sandy soils of this area developed on the Poole Formation. Initially they were nutrient-poor and acidic, but with the further clearance of woodland, these deficiencies became more marked with the loss of further nutrients and increasing acidity. Such impoverished soils could thus only support acid-tolerant species, and the main plant associations of the heathland were initially established. The continuing use of the heath for cultivation exacerbated the changes that had begun. Heather, gorse and bracken were now well established as the essential plants of the heathland. Each had its particular use for the settlers on the heathland: heather was used for thatching and broom making, bracken was used for bedding for animals and gorse was cut to provide fuel from the older stems and fodder from the young shoots. Turf was cut from the heath, and peat was dug from the low-lying marshy and boggy areas.

John Claridge, an itinerant traveller visiting Dorset in 1793, spoke of the heathlands as a 'dreary waste' of 'furze, fern and ling'. Heathland ecology reveals itself as something far more interesting and attractive than Claridge's brief and summary dismissal of the heathland scene. Dry heath is found on the well-drained sandy and gravel soils that developed after the original forest was cleared. The common heath or ling is the dominant plant, with its pale mauve flowers, together with the less common bell heather, with its brighter purple flowers. Dwarf gorse is another component of the plant community, with the larger western gorse making its appearance in places.

Bell heather, Hartland Moor.

Common gorse, winter-flowering, adds a touch of colour when the rest of the heath may appear drab, and uninteresting. Of the grasses, the fine-leaved bristle bent is the most common. The quickly spreading bracken is also abundant. In the wetter areas of the valley bottoms, and in hollows where a lens of clay produces damp conditions, wet heath takes over. Bog masses now appear, and ling and bell heather are replaced with cross-leaved heather, with its grey-green leaves. Bristle bent is replaced with purple moor grass. Bog ashphodel, several sedges and rushes, together with the different sundews make their appearance in the wet heath. Rarer plants that are found in the low-lying wet heath are the Dorset heath, and the well known marsh gentian. Peat bogs, developed over the very wettest areas introduce further variety to the heathland landscape, with various mosses and the white fluffy flowers of common cotton grass adding a distinctive element to the dampest areas. Purbeck's Hartland Moor National Nature Reserve, lying between the afforested Slepe Heath to the north and Langton Wallis to the south carries fine examples of all three of the habitats described here.

In recent years the rapid decline in the acreage of heathland has become a matter of increasing concern. Since the early nineteenth century some 86% of Dorset's heathlands has been lost, and the surviving area has become broken up to the extent that there are now more than 150 different fragments. Apart from the losses to other forms of land use, the greatest threat at the present time is the invasion of heathland by scrub. Pine, birch, willow and rhododendron, if allowed to spread uncontrolled will shade out heathland plants and eventually kill them. Under the old forms of husbandry, grazing by farm animals, the cutting of gorse and turf, and limited burning helped to maintain heathland communities in an ecologically healthy state. When these forms of farm activity ceased, the heathland plant associations became neglected and scrub began to invade considerable areas.

The Dorset Heathland Project was set up in 1989; at this time there were some 13,800 acres of heathland in Dorset, and additionally 4000 acres that had been severely affected by the invasion of scrub. An initial target was to increase the area of healthy heathland by 10% – a target that was reached two years early in 1996, and further progress has been made since that date. Pine, birch and rhododendron are cleared, the residual layers of pine needles and dead vegetation are removed. Heather seeds that have been buried are allowed to germinate and recolonise the newly cleared area. Heather is also mowed to create a mosaic of different ages and varying heights providing different habitats for heathland wildlife. Heather that has been cut, which is seed-rich, can be used for regeneration of heathland where it has disappeared. Bracken can be controlled using a herbicide. In recent years Purbeck has been one of the two principal areas in which the Heathland Project has been operating. Areas along the Furzebrook road leading south out of Stoborough have been successfully managed. The number of breeding pairs of damselflies has increased from 30 to 200 during the years of regeneration of heathland in this area. Currently the Heathland Project is working on Grange Heath within the Lulworth Ranges in conjunction with the Ministry of Defence. On Hartland Moor, one of the National Nature Reserves, an interesting experiment has been carried out where some low quality farmland has been returned to heathland with a fair measure of success. The National Trust has been responsible for returning low grade farmland to heathland at Harmony Farm near Studland, and is beginning a similar project at Greenlands Farm near Ferry Road.

Arne Nature Reserve notice, with the Dartford Warbler.

Clearly, the survival of wildlife is dependent on the continued health of the heathland community. Bird life, in particular, needs safe and secure habitats, with species such as the nightjar, the stonechat, the woodlark and the Dartford Warbler needing the right kind of heathland environment in which to live and breed. Small and young thickets of gorse are essential for the survival of the Dartford Warbler, and current management techniques ensure that this environment survives. Both the nightjar and the woodlark are ground-nesters and need reasonably open heathland, with perhaps some older heather also available. The stonechat is another heathland bird that does need young gorse thickets for its survival. The sand lizard seeks a special environment within heathland, preferring bare sunny south-facing slopes within the heathland. This niche can often be the result of past activities of man within the area: it is thus clear that a complete cover of heather is not always necessary for the successful survival of wildlife on the heath. Some 80% of the national population of sand lizards is found in Dorset, and 90% of the smooth snake population is found within the county.

Man has no doubt been responsible for the evolution of the heathland community as we see it today, clearing the forests of northern Purbeck, and establishing farming communities throughout the heathland. Liming became an important method of heath reclamation, although Thomas Hardy described the consequences of cultivating such land with some foreboding. 'The man who discovered it could be tilled died of labour, the man who succeeded him in possession ruined himself in fertilising it'. Heathcroppers, as the subsistence farmers were known, were a tough and hardy breed. They were able to market their surplus products in Wareham or other neighbouring communities, but land carved from the heath rarely allowed a comfortable living. Some settlements have survived well such as Scotland Farm to the north of Corfe Castle, built of sturdy Purbeck stone, some no doubt taken from the remains of the castle to the south(a date carved in the stone above the lintel is 1665, some twenty years after the partial destruction of the castle). The fertile alluvium of the neighbouring Corfe River offered better soils than the nutrient poor heathland ones and this is perhaps one key to the survival of Scotland. There is evidence enough of abandoned farms in the heathland, but others survive, particularly along the shores of Poole Harbour, where soils are marginally better, with Greenlands evocatively suggesting pastures amongst the drab nature of the surrounding heath. Today it is not uncommon to see a field of maize, a particularly demanding crop, standing and surviving well on privileged plots on the heathland. Perhaps the attempts to convert low grade farmland back to heathland on the edge of Hartland Moor suggest a more realistic view of the potential of the heathland for farming in the twenty-first century. Piecemeal reclamation of the heath produced its own distinct landscape in the past but it barely survives today.

Scotland Farm.

Of all of man's activities, the extraction of ball clay has probably had the greatest impact on the landscape of the heathlands. The name 'ball clay' may have two possible origins: the clay may originally have been dug out and formed into rough ball shapes, or the name may come from the tubals, the tools used to dig out the clay. Ball clay was originally derived from the weathering of the Dartmoor granite some 80 miles to the west of the Dorset deposits. The feldspar in the granite is weathered to form kaolinite, and this fine clay was carried eastwards by rivers from the Dartmoor area into Dorset where it was deposited in what were temporary shallow lakes. The clay occurs as lenses within the Poole Formation, which underlies much of the heathlands of Purbeck There are two belts of ball clay underlying the heathlands: one runs from East Holme

Old ball clay mine, Cotness.

to Ridge, and another to the south runs from Povington to Rempstone. Ball clay seems to have been worked in Purbeck since Roman times, and for hundreds of years it was used locally to produce good quality china and earthenware. It first became of national importance with the rise of the ceramics industry in the late eighteenth century, when Josiah Wedgwood in Staffordshire began to show an interest in the high quality clay produced from the Dorset deposits. For centuries the clay was either won from open-cast pits or from shallow mines which were driven in as adits at a shallow angle. In the twenty-first century all of the mines have now been closed . The last closures took place in 1999 when the mines at Aldermoor and Norden ceased to produce. Production is concentrated in six large pits, although strictly speaking the most northerly of the pits, the one at Trigon to the north of Wareham is not really in Purbeck. Today total production varies from year to year between 180,000 to 200,000 tons, with Dorey's Farm, near Stoborough producing 60,000 tons and Povington in the Lulworth Ranges producing 45,000 tons.

Dorey's Farm ball clay pit.

Commercial working of ball clay first began on a large scale in the eighteenth century. The Hyde family from Poole worked the ball clays around Arne, and supplied Josiah Wedgwood with high quality clay from the Rempstone estate. Much of it was shipped out from Hyde's Quay on Poole Harbour, of which little trace remains today.

In 1760, the Pike brothers from Devon bought Furzebrook House as a centre for mining activity. Their operations expanded steadily to include workings over much of the heathland in the western part of Purbeck from Grange and Holme Heaths in the west to Stoborough in the east. Benjamin Fayle, a London potter began his workings around Norden in 1795. He was also responsible for building the tramway to Middlebere Quay, which gave him access to tidewater for the shipping out of his ball clay. The Pike brothers had to follow suit, and opened a line from Furzebrook to Ridge Quay on the Frome.

Fayle turned towards the eastern heathlands in the next stage of exploitation, and began to open up deposits near Newton, with a linking railway to Goathorn on Poole Harbour. At Goathorn sea-going vessels could be loaded direct since it was located on South Deep which allowed larger vessels to come right in to the pier. In 1905, a new line connected the workings at Norden to Goathorn – Middlebere was fast silting up, and became redundant with the building of the new line. Inevitably the Pike and Fayle companies could only survive if they amalgamated, and they joined forces in 1949. Gradually the little railways fell into disuse, and the last line, to Eldon sidings near Corfe closed in 1970. English China Clays took over operations in 1968, and the French company Imerys gained control of all of the Purbeck operation in 1999. Almost 80% of production is now exported, mostly through Poole, although occasionally Teignmouth is used as the export port, and some is even sent abroad in containers. Production is expanding at 2-3% a year, and available deposits suggest a continued life for ball clay production of at least twenty-five years.

Autumn reflections, Norden Woods.

Past and present production have combined to produce a distinctive ball clay landscape in the Purbeck heathlands. Much of the land to the west of the Wareham – Corfe Castle road is pock-marked with old workings, some relatively small, others such as the Blue Pool, one of the Pike brothers original workings, considerably larger. Many of the pits are now overgrown and obscured by the inevitable growth of scrub, particularly in the area between Creech, where the largest body of water, Breach Pond is found, and Norden, where two pits lie either side of the main road. All of the disused pits have attracted a varied and often rare wildlife, and now have an important conservation value, such as the sand lizard habitat at Green Pool on the road from Furzebrook to East Creech.

The larger pits have a huge impact on the landscape, none more so than that at Povington, opened in 1949 and totally within the Lulworth Ranges. Clearly visible from the road that runs along the crest of the western Purbeck Hills, it is still one of the largest opencast sites in Dorset. The grey and often iron-stained sides of the pit contrast markedly with the tawny browns and pastel greens of the surrounding heath and copse. The Arne pit, on the edge of Poole Harbour, is by comparison well hidden from view, with a huge protective bund on the harbour side of the workings. Dorey's Farm, the most recent of the newer pits, occupies a site to the west of Stoborough. The extension of the Squirrel's Cottage pit to the north-west of Dorey's Farm was refused on environmental and ecological grounds. Dorey's Farm was a second option where good quality heathland was not affected, no SSSI was involved and the main archaeological site, Three Lords' Barrow was just outside the proposed working area. Furzey Ground, just to the west of the main processing works at Furzebrook, is still worked for ball clay but combines other uses with the extraction. Clay from other pits is stockpiled here to await orders from customers, and the necessary blending. Waste from the processing works is also stored here. Although Furzey Ground has something of the aspect of a lunar landscape, with pits, stockpiles, and debris heaps, it will be restored to heathland when it ceases to have any commercial use.

Restoration of the pit sites once they have been worked out now has a very high profile. Present workings will not contribute to the pock-marked landscape of old workings that

Squirrel's Cottage ball clay pit, 1990.

Restoration of Squirrel's Cottage ball clay pit, 1996.

is so familiar to the north and west of Corfe Castle. Each site will be carfully landscaped and then restored to heathland. Once the site has been landscaped it is then re-seeded using the seeds from the mowings of RSPB reserves in the north of Purbeck. Squirrel's Cottage was once one of the largest pits in Purbeck and ceased production in the 1990s. During its working life Squirrel's Cottage itself was demolished in order to work the clay beneath: a new four-bedroomed house was built by E.C.C. to replace it. Today it is a tranquil area of grassland and heathland amongst the pines just off the road from Stoborough to East Holme, with a lake enclosing a small island. Plans are now going ahead to create a ball clay museum at Norden, once the centre of the industry in the Corfe Castle area, adding a new element to the landscape in that area.

The exploitation of the petroleum in the Wytch Farm oilfield is the latest of man's activities to have an impact on the landscape of the heathlands. Oil was first produced in Purbeck from the small well on the cliffs at Kimmeridge that has been producing since 1959.This well has far exceeded expectation; it was given an original life of about twenty-five years, but it is now still producing nearly fifty years on. The oil is taken by road tanker to the gathering station at Wytch Farm.

Oil wells, Wytch Farm.

Developing what turned out to be the largest onshore oilfield in Europe in an area such as the Purbeck heathlands presented a whole series of ecological and conservation challenges to British Petroleum. Attention has had to be paid to integrating the development of the oilfield with the landscape of the Purbeck heathlands Careful use of the existing topography to shield or obscure developments has been combined with the colour treatment of surfaces and the planting of local species to minimise the impact of the exploration and development programme.

The oil is produced from three main reservoirs at depth in the Purbeck Heathlands and Furzey Island in Poole Harbour. The first to be discovered in 1974 was the Bridport Reservoir, at a depth of 900 metres (3000 feet), and with a peak production of 6000 barrels a day, nearly 80% of the reservoir's potential has now been tapped. The Sherwood Reservoir at a depth of nearly 1600 metres (5250 feet) has a much greater potential – nearly thirty times as large, although only a half of this is likely to be recovered with present technology. The Frome Reservoir is a much smaller proposition, with only 50 million barrels potential.

Peak production in the Wytch Farm oilfield was reached in the late 1990s at 110,000 barrels per day: the field is now in decline and produced about 30,000 barrels per day in the middle years of the first decade of the twenty-first century.

Drilling rig, Goathorn Peninsula.

Nearly all of the producing wells are found in a zone that runs from just south of Wytch Farm to the Goathorn peninsula, with outlying ones off the road from Ridge to Arne, and on Furzey Island. The nodding donkey has become a familiar part ot the heathland scene to those used to following the tracks through the forests and along their northern edges. To the casual visitor to Purbeck the impact of the oilfield is likely to pass quite unnoticed. However, to those travelling along Ferry Road from Studland to Sandbanks, whether commuters in winter or tourists in summer, the drilling rig on the Goathorn Peninsula is a reminder of the on-going nature of oil exploration. From the site in the centre of the Goathorn Peninsula extended-reach drilling has been carried out in order to exploit the vast reserves of oil underneath Poole Harbour and in the western part of Poole Bay. The Goathorn Peninsula is particularly sensitive ecologically: much of the peninsula is a S.S.S.I., together with the neighbouring mudflats of Poole Harbour, and fulfils all of the criteria for a European Union Special Protection area. Amongst the rare species found on the peninsula are the nightjar, the sand lizard and the smooth snake and the Dorset heath, all set within a matrix of dry heath, acid grassland and broad-leaved woodland. Goathorn's essential natural landscape is a mosaic of pine and deciduous woodland heath, saltmarsh, mudflats and tidal water. Two well sites now exist on Goathorn: well site F was long established, and safely screened by mature pine woodland; the new well site M is the site for extended reach drilling. An Environmental Statement, and a non-technical summary were required by the planning regulations: B.P. were able to show that this site was not of unique ecological value. Nevertheless B.P. were required to manage 64 acres of Goathorn for nature conservation over the life of the oilfield. So Goathorn, busy once with the rumble of trucks bringing ball clay to the pier on South Deep, now echoes to the more sophisticated hum of extended reach drilling in the twenty-first century. Its tranquil southern shore, with its small white sandy beaches, looks across the mudflats of Brands Bay to the South Haven Peninsula and busy Ferry Road.

The whole of the B.P. operation has succeeded in exploiting the oil resource without undue ecological and environmental impact. All of the oil wells are hidden away in that area between Rempstone Forest and the patchwork farmland on the southern shores of Poole Harbour. The vast Gathering Station just to the south of Wytch Farm is well screened by the woods of Corsican Pine that surround it and the rail depot at Furzebrook is so well hidden behind a huge bund that few would know of its existence. So the landscape of the nodding donkey, the drilling rig and the hidden major installations had become part of the heathland scene in the late twentieth century. With the oilfield entering its final stages of exploitation, a future without these landscape elements is not difficult to envisage, such have been B.P.'s care and attention to the landscape upon which they have briefly intruded.

Two of Purbeck's country houses lie towards the southern end of the heathlands. In the west Creech Grange lies in the shadow of the densely wooded northern slopes of the Purbeck Hills, partly hidden by the trees that have been planted on either side of the drive. Although the east front can be glimpsed through the wrought iron gates on the Stoborough road, the finest view of the Grange is obtained from the steep road that ascends the Purbeck Hills to the south. Originally it was a grange or farm of Bindon Abbey, but after the Dissolution of the Monasteries it passed eventually to Sir Oliver Lawrence who rebuilt it as a manor house. The house was sold to the Bond family in 1691, and they were responsible for considerable alterations to the house over a period of nearly two centuries, including a rebuilding of the front in 1846. The tiny chapel of St John the Evangelist, located on a knoll to the north-west of the Grange, was first built in 1746, but it was enlarged in1849 and finally consecrated in 1859. Rempstone Hall, nearly 6 miles to the east, also lies in the shadow of the wooded northern slopes of the Purbeck Hills just to the north of Ailwood Down. It is set amidst woods and a small lake from which a stream trickles northwards into Foxground plantation. It was originally bought as a farmhouse by John Calcraft in 1757: he spent time and money in improving the farmhouse to a more imposing building. It passed eventually to a Captain Marston, and later to the Ryder family.

Creech Grange.

The natural heathland landscape is not unique to Purbeck, since it also exists farther to the north and west in the Frome and Piddle lowlands. However, with man's exploitation of the resources of the Purbeck heathland over the time since early civilisations first began to clear the primeval woodland, a distinct landscape of sequent occupance

Studland Heath, looking east.

The Blue Pool.

Studland Heath, looking north

has been created. Today there is remarkable mosaic of landscapes between Luckford Lake and the eastern dune-girt shores of the heathland. Large tracts of natural heathland still remain in the west in the land of the Lulworth Ranges, and also in the east where National Nature Reserves in Stoborough Heath, Hartland Moor, Studland and Godlingston Heaths display heathland and its varied flora and fauna of the very highest ecological quality. Here, the primeval landscape so beloved of Hardy and Treves remains almost unaltered: the Agglestone and Puckstone in a late summer dusk, with wisps of mist settling in the shallow valleys with their yellowing moor grass create the same impression of timelessness that impressed Hardy and Treves. Farmland patchily survives along the roads that cross Purbeck from the Frome lowlands to the Chalk ridge and beyond; beyond the coniferous forests farms still add a green strip along the southern shores of Poole Harbour, where all the once busy ball clay ports are now silent and almost lost to antiquity. The great pits of ball clay survive, starkly in the primeval wastes of Povington, more integrated into the copse and heath of the central zone at Dorey's Farm, or quite obscured and almost unknown in the great Arne Pit on the southern shores of Poole Harbour. Hundreds of little overgrown pits survive between Norden and Creech, and the Blue Pool has made its mark on the tourist scene. Finally the exploitation of the oil resource at great depth beneath the surface has, in response to modern planning regulations, left little impact and even enhanced the heathland scene with sensitive planting of native species.

Chapter Four

The Purbeck Hills

Running from the Foreland to Flower's Barrow, overlooking Worbarrow Bay, the Purbeck Hills are the Isle's most magnificent landscape asset. The rounded contours of this Chalk ridge are one of Dorset's most familiar features: they can be seen from distant Win Green to the east of Shaftesbury as a line of blue hills on the far southern horizon; they appear to travellers across the gravel plateaux of the western New Forest as a series of billowing curves across the lowering winter skies beyond the lights of Bournemouth; from the main West Country road to the west of Dorchester they carry the eye eastwards from the Chalk uplands between Dorset's County Town and Weymouth. From space, satellite images show how they are part of the essential outline of Purbeck's landscape, appearing like a huge taut bow across the peninsula; giving a distinctive outline to its coastline both to the east and the west.

Ballard Down, with the Isle of Wight in the distance.

Their form is essentially derived from the huge geological structure produced by the Alpine earth-building movements of some twenty million years ago. In the so-called Purbeck monocline, the Jurassic and younger rocks have pushed up into a great asymmetrical upfold, with a relatively gentle limb on the southern side and far steeper dips on the northern limb. Thus the Purbeck Hills have been fashioned from steeply dipping or vertical Chalk. As a result of the folding processes, much of the Chalk is broken or fractured and often hardened to a tough, but brittle and broken rock. The Chalk is also broken by a series of faults or major fractures in the rock, which create lines of weakness in the rock which aid erosion, and may account for the directions taken by the dry valleys of the ridge. The most prominent fault is the famous Ballard Down Fault, which can only be seen from the sea where it is exposed in the cliffs to the north of Ballard Point, although it does extend for several miles inland.

The Purbeck Hills do not achieve a uniform crest line between Ballard Point and Flower's Barrow. Their surging heights reach nearly 200 metres (656feet) on Godlingston Hill to the north of Swanage, and just over 198 metres (649 feet) on Ridgeway Hill to the north-west of Church Knowle. It is the prominent gaps and high level cols that break the crestline of the hills that add so much to its character. Between

The Foreland and Flower's Barrow there are two breaks in the Purbeck Hills, and three other points where the ridge is low enough for it to be crossed by a road. The most spectacular gaps are the twin ones at Corfe Castle. Treves wrote 'The Purbeck Hills run from east to west across the isle (sic) in the form of a long rampart of smooth grass downs. In a sudden abrupt gap or gate in this Titanic barricade, stands the Castle on the summit of a precipitous mound'. Treves was not quite accurate in his description, because there are two gaps at Corfe, not one. Two little streams, the Byle Brook, and the Corfe River itself have cut these gaps in the high Chalk ridge, isolating the entirely natural hillock on which the castle is built. The Byle Brook gap on the east, has the steeper sides, and is probably the one that Treves had in mind when he used the word 'abrupt'. In the western gap the Corfe River curves away from West Hill leaving a steep slope beyond the remains of West Mill. This slope is almost certainly a meander scar, indicating where the river flowed at some time during its past history.

The Ulwell Gap is quite different to the gap at Corfe. It is cut down between the steep slopes that lead up to Godlingston Hill to the west and the western part of Ballard

The Corfe Gaps seen from Corfe Common to the south.

Down to the east, surmounted by the granite obelisk. A small stream rises near Ulwell Farm to the south of the gap, and flows south-eastwards to enter the sea at the northern end of Shore Road in Swanage, after flowing through a culvert for the latter part of its course. It is possible that this tiny stream rose further up in the gap at one time. At the far western end of Purbeck an equally tiny stream still flows through the gap at Arish Mell, once again bounded by very steep slopes one either side. All three of the high level cols, at Tyneham, Lutton and Cocknowle indicate where small streams may have flowed northwards at one time, possibly as southern extensions of present day streams to the north that now flow into the Frome. Every single one of these streams flows across the east-west geological grain of Purbeck, unusual, but not unknown – there is a similar situation with the streams in the Isle of Wight. It is tempting to regard all of the streams that flow today, or flowed in the past, as part of an ancient pattern where all of Purbeck's streams may have flowed to the north across a plain cut by the sea millions of years ago, and then uplifted.

The gaps in the Purbeck Hills serve to divide the ridge into stretches of beautifully curved crestlines that have their own distinctive character. The stretch from Ballard Point to the Ulwell gap is probably the nearest that is found in Purbeck to the famed open downland, of the Chalk with short cropped grass, nibbled by countless sheep over the years. It is perhaps more open than the hills to the west, and the majestic views from its crest will forever be enshrined in the words of E. M. Forster in *Howards' End* – 'If one wanted to show a foreigner England, perhaps the wisest course would be to take him to the final section of the Purbeck Hills, and stand him on their summit... then system after system of our island would roll together under his feet...' The long run of the hills from Ulwell to Corfe Castle has an essentially different character. Increasingly fenced in, it does not have quite the same sense of freedom as Ballard Down, nor are the views quite as entrancing as the great sweep of sea and distant shoreline that is Ballard's own panorama. However, Ailwood Down with its rich endowment of prehistoric burial sites is the great treasure of this stretch of the Hills. Farther to the west, as Corfe Castle is approached, the views, particularly to the south are true Purbeck, with the intimacy of copse and pasture in the Vale to the south beguiling the eye and bringing a sense of rural calm to the urban mind.

Beyond the dramatic gaps at Corfe, the remoteness of western Purbeck begins to exert its easeful influence. Fewer tourists or school parties tread the path from West Mill up on to Knowle Hill and across the crest to the gap at Cocknowle, still of mysterious origin. Beyond Cocknowle all is true west Purbeck: Creech Barrow dominates to the north and Steeple's cluster of houses and its manor rest peacefully, half-hidden amongst the vale's hedgerows and thickets. Beyond the Steeple car park, the land is suddenly forbidden and the Lulworth Ranges, with red flags and warning notices create a new foreboding atmosphere on the ridge of the hills. Although the ridgetop road is usually open, the footpaths lie closed for much of the year, only to bring renewed pleasure when the view of the Tyneham Vale and the western heaths can be appreciated on weekends and in the holidays. Along the track ascending Whiteway Hill new views open across the green pastures on either side of Tyneham's gwyle and distant Portland becomes almost part of the west Purbeck scene. Flower's Barrow, as rich in prehistory as Ailwood, is west Purbeck's culminating pleasure. Its views did not perhaps impress E.M. Forster in the way that Ballard's did, but the cliffscapes of Worbarrow, Arish and Mupe are without parallel in southern England.

The path from Old Harry Rocks and The Foreland to Ballard Down passes firstly across Old Nicks Ground and then rises steadily to the easternmost slopes of Ballard Down itself. Much of this area is now open Chalk downland, the turf having been restored from land that had been under the plough – an attempt by the National

View looking north from Ballard Down.

View looking south from Ballard Down.

Trust to create a more 'natural' landscape in this coastal area. Following the crest of the ridge westwards the old Ordnance Survey Triangulation Post lies close to a cross ridge dyke. The latter is not thought to be of any great antiquity (although it is not dissimilar to features first developed in the Iron Age). It is almost certainly a structure dating from the Second World War, including an RAF Control Point for an air-to-ground firing range.

The views to the north and south now begin to open up and E.M. Forster's claim can be examined in a little more detail. Immediately to the north of Ballard Down and the declining Chalk slopes to the north is the sandstone ridge that runs inland from Redend Point, prominent first in the pine-clad Woodhouse Hill and later to the west in Dean Hill. Beyond is the village of Studland, mostly hidden by trees, and then the South Haven Peninsula attracts the attention of the eye. In the fading light of a winter's afternoon the arcuate form of the different sand dune ridges on the eastern side of the peninsula stands out quite clearly. Little Sea, now quite cut off from Studland Bay, lies to the west and beyond is the old sea cliff of 400 or more years ago, forming the eastern edge of Studland Heath and the narrow belt of land that carries Ferry Road to the Sandbanks Ferry. Poole Harbour with its wooded islands lies beyond, reminding us of the post-glacial rise in sea level that drowned so many of the lower river valleys of southern England. Urban Dorset lies on the far side of the harbour's waters, with Poole and Bournemouth partly hidden within the abundant pines still left on what was once part of Dorset's primeval heath. Inland the urban areas run away to the horizons of Cranborne Chase, and the darker conifers of the New Forest to the east.

If the coastline is followed around to the east, Poole Bay's urbanised cliffs, now seldom bare, but clad in landslide-preventing grasses shrubs and exotic trees, fall away to the low isthmus that connects Southbourne to Hengistbury Head. Here Tertiary sands and clays are often bright in the sun on the south-facing cliffs. Further still are the cliffs of Highcliffe and Hampshire's Barton-on-Sea, the latter still unstable despite many attempts to tame their obstinate geology. They end in another graceful curve that takes in the shingle structure of Hurst Castle Spit, with its white lighthouse just visible.The far horizon here carries the power station at Fawley on Southampton Water, and to its left the chimneys and installations of Esso's Fawley refinery and petrochemical plants.

The Ulwell Gap.

Forster would have included the Isle of Wight in his 'systems that roll together'. Opposite Ballard Point, some fifteen kilometres (9½ miles) to the east are the Needles and the always-bright Chalk of Scratchell's Bay. All of the Isle of Wight can be seen in profile – the central Chalk ridge, the continuation of the Purbeck Hills, and to the north, the northern lowlands of the island, underlain by Tertiary sands and clays, often with a carapace of later gravels. To the south are Wight's central lowlands carved out of Cretaceous sands and clays, dominated to the south by the southern Chalk and Greensand uplands that overlook Ventnor and its landslipped coasts. At one time the Chalk ridge of Purbeck was linked to that of the Isle of Wight, but there is little agreement yet as to the date of the breaching of this ridge that opened up the old Solent River's lowlands to erosion.

To the south there is another entrancing view, even if it is less all-embracing. Swanage Bay, cut in easily eroded clays, shales and sands, curves round from Punfield Cove to Peveril Point where the harder rocks of the upper Purbeck Beds outcrop. Shore Road, Swanage's seafront, forms a central focus to the view of Swanage. To the north buildings are precariously perched on the edge of the eroding and slipping cliffs: nearer, New Swanage rests more safely at a greater distance from the cliff edge. Beyond Shore Road Swanage's seaside businesses stretch away to the pierhead, and villas and newer apartments climb away towards Durlston. Recent growth around Herston has pushed up towards the now abandoned quarries and mines that supplied so much of the stone that was exported from Swanage in the nineteenth century. Purbeck stretches away to the west: the limestone upland, pock-marked with small quarries and riven with the larger ones, runs away to St Aldhelm's Head; the Vale of Purbeck, here all billowing curvy hillocks leads us away to Corfe and West Purbeck, with Kingston's church looking down from its surround of trees.

Westwards from this viewpoint the path continues until the track from Studland comes up from the north, and descends to Whitecliff Farm to the south. By the side of this track is a long oblong stone block, with the now faint words 'Rest and be Thankful' carved in it. It was set up by a Dr Jardine in 1852, with the date again just visible. The crestal path is now rising all of the time until the summit of Ballard Down is reached: a slight descent and Ballard's other monument, visible from the Corfe to Studland road is encountered. George Burt first erected this obelisk in 1892, to celebrate the inauguration of Swanage's water supply. It was feared that it would be a guide to enemy aircraft in the Second World War, so it was temporarily demolished. It was re-erected again in 1973 by the Royal Engineers.

From the granite obelisk the Ulwell gap, which carries the road to Studland the Sandbanks Ferry comes into view. No stream flows in the gap now, but no doubt exists that it was cut by a stream that rose in the shadow of Dean Hill to the north. It is entirely possible that the whole gap was cut by a much larger stream that flowed to the north, but there is little present day evidence for this. The feature that catches the eye

The granite obelisk, Ballard Down.

The Rest and Be Thankful stone bench.

Giant's Grave Bottom.

is the remarkable valley of Giant's Grave Bottom. This deeply cut dry valley heads steeply under Godlingston Hill and then extends south-eastwards before turning through a right angle and trending north-eastwards to join the main Ulwell Gap

The valley was probably initially cut in pre-glacial times, but deepened in periglacial times. During this latter period the heights of Godlingston Hill would have carries sizeable snow patches and during the early summer meltwater from these snow-patches would have coursed down from Godlingston Hill and carved this valley on its south-eastern flanks.The marked change in direction of Giant's Grave Bottom is probably the result of the initial pre-glacial stream following different lines of weakness in the Chalk as the valley developed. The lines of weakness may be major fractures such as faults or, more likely, joints, which are much smaller fissures within the Chalk.

Bronze Age barrows, Ailwood Down.

Godlingston Hill stands proudly as the highest point in the stretch of the Purbeck Hills between Ulwell and Corfe Castle. Sadly, it is no longer accessible to the walker, and is now the preserve of masts and communications equipment. In its southern face is a large hollow, just below the track that rises from Round Down to the crest of the ridge. There are several others, notably to the east of the Ulwell gap. These are nivation hollows: where snow accumulated in hollows on the Chalk ridge in periglacial times: freezing and thawing around the edges of the hollows would have gradually extended them, the angular debris from this action being carried downslope from the hollow by gravity controlled movement. Geology maps show that the debris was often carried well out into the vale to the south. The crestline of the hills falls away to the west, passing several gnarled hawthorns bent before the wind – evidence of the exposure to the strong south-westerlies that sweep across the Purbeck Hills from the Channel Coast to the south. More open land leads on through gorse bushes to Ailwood Down, with its long barrow and whole series of round barrows.

This is a special place, again commanding magnificent views both to the north and to the south. To the north, the whole of Poole Harbour, with its many ramifying inlets and creeks, lies spread out before the observer standing on one of the round barrows. A late evening view, after the sun has gone, often gives an almost opalescent sheen to the still waters of the harbour. To the south of the harbour the conifers of Rempstone Forest mask all of the former heathland and the installations of the Wytch Farm oilfield. To the south the view takes in all of Purbeck's wealden vale, and the linear houses of Harman's Cross, with perhaps a glimpse of a passing cloud of steam, and Purbeck's own train running through copse and cutting.

Although Nine Barrow Down is clearly marked on the Ordnance Survey Map, the great burial site lies to the north-west on Ailwood Down. Furthermore, there are eighteen barrows here altogether – seventeen round barrows and one long barrow. The Neolithic long barrow stretches east-west, following the trend of the ridge top, but built slightly off the crest line with the burial chamber facing east. It is located slightly below the ridge top so that it is 'skyline visible' from the south. Ten Bronze Age round barrows are located on the crestline so that they could be seen from both the north and the south. The two largest and most impressive round barrows are close to the long barrow, and were possible built deliberately to overshadow the older structure in a dominant way. Some smaller round barrows lie to the south off the ridge crest and are probably of a later age than the ones built on the ridge crest. An air of mystery still pervades this burial site of the new Stone Age and the Bronze Age which reminds us of the now distant life and death of past civilisations.

Rollington dry valley.

Descending the flint-strewn track from Ailwood Down the view embraces all of the Purbeck Vale stretching away to distant Tyneham, with the ridge curving towards Corfe Castle and then sweeping on to the heights of Knowle Hill and Ridgeway Hill. Brenscombe Hill has its two small dry valleys hidden in the woodlands on the northern side of the ridge, the eastern one giving access to the Rempstone Stone Circle just below the ridge, with its Bronze Age date suggesting a cultural connection with the burial mounds on Ailwood. Woodlands form an almost continuous zone along the northern flanks of the Purbeck Hill in this stretch between Ulwell and Corfe, forming attractive 'hangers' from King's Wood in the east to Bushey Wood in the west. After

Looking west from Ailwood Down.

Rollington Hill's television and communication mast, another dry valley runs away to the north towards Rollington Farm, carrying an ancient way that comes up from Little Woolgarston to the south, and extends north past Rollington Farm to become Thrasher's Lane as it cuts through the conifers to Wytch Farm and possibly the little port that once existed on Wych Lake.

From the television transmitter, Challow Hill lies just to the west and beyond lies East Hill with its steep drop down into the gap cut by the little Byle Brook. From East Hill there is a view of one of the classic landscapes of Purbeck. Corfe Castle has become symbolic of Purbeck in many respects, and appears in countless logos and letterheads. The hillock isolated by the deep valleys of the two little rivers is a natural defensive site. Although there is some evidence of earlier occupation, all of today's ruined fortifications date from Norman times. It grew steadily from the first structures built by William The Conqueror in 1080, with the keep being added in 1105, together with further defences enclosing the inner bailey. Expansion westwards saw the completion of defences surrounding the spur that runs towards the valley of the Corfe.

Further expansion took place downslope to the south-east: the great ditch was built and new walls and bastions enclosed the outer bailey, and finally the main entrance gateway was constructed with the bridge across the moat. After 1300 the castle was not always kept in a good state of repair and parts became dilapidated but expensive repairs became necessary and were carried out during the later years of the reign of

Corfe Castle and West Hill.

Corfe Castle, East Hill and Challow Hill.

Edward III and later the new gloriette tower began to take shape in Richard II's reign. More repairs were needed at the beginning of the sixteenth century. After the loss of the castle to the Parliamentarians in 1646, the Commons voted for the demolition of the castle. Such was the strength of the construction of the castle that no demolition could ever be completely successful. In the National Trust Guide of 1987 we read '…The castle as we know it today is a testimony to the skill of the sappers, the power of the explosives and the strength and quality of a building which had developed as a royal castle over five centuries'. Treves sums it up admirably and succinctly 'The castle is still magnificent.'

The Chalk ridge west of Corfe.

Beyond the gap cut by the Corfe River, with the ruins of West Mill, operating from the late thirteenth century to the early twentieth century, the Purbeck Hills rise again towards the west. Two small hollows in the south face of the ridge merit attention : these are again nivation hollows, similar to the one under Godlingston Hill. Knowle Hill has its own hanger wood on the northern side, overlooking the old clay workings to the west of Norden. On the southern side of Knowle Hill is the partly restored limekiln, where chalk from the abandoned quarry above was calcined and then mixed with sand from the pits on Corfe Common to produce builders' mortar. Expansive views open up over Church Knowle village to the south across to the long dip slope of the limestone plateau to the south and Smedmore Hill's distant skyline. To the south-east of Church Knowle, Bucknowle House makes its appearance, built on its own patch of well-drained river gravels. The fecundity of this part of the vale always seems to be most noticeable in late summer, when the number of maize fields seems to proliferate every year. Westwards the sullen bulk of Creech Barrow begins to make its presence felt beyond Stonehill Down and Cocknowle's dry valley. Creech Barrow does over-look the ridge and is really quite separate from it geologically speaking. It is capped by a small patch of rubbly limestone – at one time thought to be of similar age to that at Bembridge in the Isle of Wight, but now thought to be older and the same age as the Barton Clay that forms the middle section of the cliffs at Hengistbury Head to the east of Bournemouth.

Creech Barrow.

Cocknowle's gap is the most interesting and puzzling of all of the breaks in the ridge. The col where the minor road crosses the ridge has to be seen as part of the sequence of breaks in the continuity of the ridge where north-flowing streams flowed in parallel fashion across an uplifted marine plain. The Cocknowle stream, like several others such as the ones that crossed near Lutton and Tyneham has now become dismembered because of the manner in which the drainage pattern developed in the vale to the south. What is quite remarkable about the Cocknowle Gap is the existence of a longi-

The Purbeck Hills, looking east from Ridgeway Hill.

Cocknowle and Creech Barrow.

tudinal dry valley parallel to the ridge, followed by the minor road after its zigzag bend. The valley suddenly makes a sharp turn to the north and exits from the ridge in a gorge-like defile. Is this valley similar in origin to Giant's Grave Bottom on the western side of the Ulwell Gap? Is it fault-guided, with the fault being a response to the tremendous pressure from the south during the Alpine earth movements of twenty million year ago? The abrupt sides of the gorge certainly suggest that this is the case. In common with Giant's Grave Bottom it was no doubt deepened in periglacial times by spring and early summer meltwaters. Most of the upper part of the dry valley lies within a Dorset Wildlife Trust Nature Reserve.

The track westwards from Cocknowle runs parallel to the Stonehill dry valley and gently upwards. Passing through the gates overlooking Whiteway Farm the old boundary stone between Church Knowle and Steeple is seen with its crude carvings of 'K' and 'S'. Great Wood, perhaps the most spectacular hanger of all, appears on the northern side of Ridgeway Hill. In the open scrub between the path and Great Wood

The limekiln, Church Knowle.

bluebells bloom in spring in a profusion seldom surpassed in Purbeck, well set off by the yellow of the ubiquitous gorse and the pink of the first campions.

Bluebells in Great Wood.

Grange Arch, Denis Bond's 1740 folly, is all pillars and arches, and looks down through the gap in Great Wood to Creech Grange. Just off the ridge crest, it is well displayed for the inhabitants of Creech Grange. Now managed by the National Trust, its surrounds are well manicured, and it remains one of Purbeck's idiosyncracies, although not perhaps the best known. The ridgeway track surges on westwards, and emerges at the Steeple car park, one of two on the ridgetop (the other is at Povington Hill). The ridgetop now, for the first time carries a road, albeit closed when firing will not allow the passage of vehicles: a Range Walk runs parallel to it easing walkers through the forbidden territory of the ranges. From the walk the lost lands of Tyneham's farms, seemingly greener and more lush than any other of the vale's lands to the east, lie spread out before the observer. Here the infant Corfe rises, to begin its short journey to Poole Harbour, and just on the other side of the North Egliston watershed, the Tyneham gwyle stream begins its trickle towards the sea at Worbarrow Bay. Beyond Povington's car park the hills begin to surge once more, and a glimpse to the north will reveal a bird's-eye view of Purbeck's biggest hole, the Povington ball clay pit,now being carefully restored at its western end.

Grange Arch.

Whiteway Hill is ascended by the ridgetop track, here flint-strewn from the underlying Upper Chalk. This is true Firing Range country – all targets, warning notices and yellow boundary posts keeping the walker within strict limits. After several blackthorn thickets, the great fortification of Flower's Barrow heaves itself into view and the western meeting of the Purbeck Hills with the sea is in sight.

Approached from the east, Flower's Barrow is at its least impressive. Only a cross profile of the rampart is revealed and the true majesty of this great hill fort is not appreciated. Once past the picnic tables and the interpretation boards, the huge views to Portland open up to the west and the closer appeal of Cow Corner's Chalk cliffs and Arish Mell's steep defile lie beneath the walker's feet. It is, of course, quite possible to walk from Old Harry Rocks along the ridgeway route to Flower's Barrow in a day: there can be no finer traverse in southern England. Apart from its southern coast almost all of Purbeck can be appreciated from this skyline route – the brown expanses of the heathland, now often covered by the green blocks of coniferous plantations, the beckoning curves and winding ridgeway of the Hills themselves, the rural intimacy of the vale below and the distant skyline of walled fields, occasional copses and remote farms of the limestone upland to the south.

Chapter Five

The Vale of Purbeck

Purbeck's central vale, quintessential rural Dorset, underlain by the sands and clays of the Wealden Beds, extends from Swanage Bay in the east to Worbarrow Bay in the west. Its fields and copses are familiar to all those that travel between Corfe Castle and Swanage along Valley Road, and also to those who drive along the less well-used road from Corfe to Kimmeridge or to Steeple and then over the Chalk ridge to either Lulworth or Wareham. It is perhaps not easy to gain a true impression of the vale from these roads. From the Chalk ridge it certainly does not have the appearance of a flat lowland area: to the west of Swanage it has the appearance of a series of small elongated hillocks; in the centre it tends to be dominated by the low ridge of Corfe Common; beyond Corfe it is still undulating, with the Corfe stream cutting through it in a well-marked course. Villages do not cluster thickly in the vale. Corfe village spreads out towards the common from the castle; to the east there is only a concentration of relatively recent settlement in Harman's Cross. West of Corfe, Church Knowle nestles just under the Chalk ridge, and Steeple, hardly a village in the strict sense, hides itself away from the road that threads through the vale. It is farms that dominate the valley, forming two lines that run at the foot of the Chalk ridge and, in the south, the so-called 'marble farms' lie near the base of the slope that rises to the stone plateau to the south.

The vale, looking towards Swanage from Godlingston Hill.

The Vale of Purbeck, looking west from Godlingston Hill.

The vale's little streams, which lie hidden from the casual visitor, create three separate basins within the lowland. In the east all of the tiny streams focus on the Swanage Brook, that enters the sea through a culvert. In the centre of the vale, the Byle Brook and the Corfe River (also known as Wicken) gather the brooks that eventually flow northwards through the gaps at Corfe Castle. In the far west, the little Tyneham stream drains westwards from near North Egliston to the sea at Worbarrow. Although a natural three fold-division of the vale might thus seem apparent, the realities of the human occupation of the vale suggest that the area east of Corfe Castle and its common is clearly different from the deeply rural area to the west beyond Corfe.

Harman's Cross from the Purbeck Hills.

So the eastern vale, with its main road threading through Harman's Cross, and its flourishing railway has an atmosphere entirely different from the more isolated farms, tiny fields and patches of woodland that are the essence of the western vale.

In the east the little Swanage Brook, which enters the sea through a culvert, drains, with its tributaries all of the area to the east of Harman's Cross, with the watershed that separates its territory from that of the Corfe River and its tributaries, running from Brenscombe Hill in the north, through the centre of Harman's Cross to just north of Acton on the southern plateau. Windmill Knap (knap-crest of a hill or rising ground) is the highest of the small hillocks in the eastern part of the vale and owes its height to one of the most easterly of the bands of sandstone that run through the Wealden Beds in an east–west direction through the vale. In Swanage itself a band of this sandstone is responsible for the higher ground on which Harrow House School is located. The ruins of the mill barn, part of the windmill complex, are still there although there is no longer any trace of the windmill that appeared on the estate map of 1776. Almost all of Harman's Cross is built on another sandstone ridge, and interestingly the settlement looks down to the north on the valley cut by headwaters of the Byle Brook, and to the south on the valley of the Downshay brook, part of the Corfe River's drainage.

West of Harman's Cross the sandstone ridges increase in number, with the most prominent one being responsible for Corfe Common to the south of the village of Corfe, and another underlying the small rise that marks the entry of Valley Road into Corfe village. The common, Dorset's largest, covering 350 acres, is the only remaining area of uncultivated land on the outcrop of the Wealden Beds in the central vale. East Common was cultivated during the Second World War as part of the 'Dig for Victory' campaign and is consequently of less ecological value than the two commons to the west, Brickyard Common and West Common. These two latter stretches of the common, uncultivated since Roman times, are not only of great interest ecologically,

Corfe Common in snow.

Sledge corrugations on Corfe Common.

but also possess important archaeological remains. On the crest of the ridge, ample evidence exists of former occupation of the common. Several prominent Bronze Age round barrows add their distinctive presence to the existence of Celtic field systems, and a possible Romano-British temple also lies just off the summit of the ridge. The crest of the ridge immediately to the west of the Kingston road has a corrugated appearance, the result of cartloads of Purbeck Marble being hauled across the common from the marble quarries at the foot of the limestone plateau to the south to the workshops in Corfe in mediaeval times. Recent clearance of gorse and bracken has made the outline of these trackways across the common much clearer. Just off the summit ridge is the common's former sandpit, worked from 1889 to 1946: the sand was mixed with lime from the Church Knowle kiln to make builder's mortar.

The ridge of the common was, until recently, covered in invasive gorse and bracken, but National Trust policy has been to introduce a programme of cutting which encourages a much more herb-rich grassland to develop once the gorse and bracken have been cleared. Swards of bent grass clothe the ridge now, interspersed with heather, giving bright patches of purple in high summer. Spring sees bluebells cast a shimmering haze over the summits of the ridge – unforgettable against the backdrop of the castle ruins to the north. Narrow valleys within the common, cut by little streams that drain to the Corfe River to the west have an outstandingly rich ecology. Mosses abound, and are enhanced by the white fluff of Cotton Grass, Bog Asphodel and Pale Butterwort. It is these wetter flushes on the Common that shelter some of the rarer fauna: rare beetles are accompanied by three extremely rare species of damselfly.

Winter pony, Corfe Common.

Today the common is managed by the National Trust, to whom it was bequeathed in 1982 from the Corfe Castle and Kingston Lacy estate of the Bankes family. The policy of The National Trust that has most affected the landscape of the common is the controlled cutting of gorse and bracken that has encouraged plants such as Devil's Bit Scabious, Camomile, Bell Heather and Tormentil to grow in their place to give a much richer grassland cover. Corfe Castle Management Committee, composed of commons rights holders, (who are allowed the grazing of animals) and village representatives, is responsible for the day-to-day running of the common. Grazing of horses and ponies keeps the grass and scrub at manageable levels and contributes much to the pleasing aspect of the common's landscape.

Two other elements of human occupation complete the landscape of the eastern vale. In the north a line of farms runs westwards from Whitecliffe under Ballard Down to Challow just to the east of Corfe Castle. In the south is the line of 'marble farms', extending westwards from Wilkswood, hidden away in dank woodland, to the openly situated Blashenwell in the west. These farms roughly mark the line of the east–west outcrop of the Purbeck Marble, and are all that remain of larger settlements where the Marble was worked in the past – Purbeck's 'lost villages'. This pattern, on the north and south of the vale, was already established in Saxon times, when today's farms marked the centre of an estate, eight on the northern side and eight on the southern side.

Godlingston Manor.

The northern farms from Godlingston Manor to Challow, located below the Chalk ridge so that they are able to cultivate the rich soils of the Greensands, are joined by a little used road that follows a switchback route under the Chalk ridge to the north. Whitecliffe, isolated away to the east under Studland Hill, was in existence in Domesday times, and was originally a manor and tithing of Swanage. Godlingston Manor, by far the grandest of the buildings in the northern line dates back to the thirteenth century. It is one of the most sturdy of Purbeck's country houses, with its distinctive trefoiled doorway and solid tower at the western end of the building, the latter balanced by a two storey east wing. Knitson, now very much the centre of country crafts, is first recorded as *Knyghtwyneston* in 1309 – 'farm of Cnightwine'.

Knaveswell, to the west, which means 'spring of water found by a youth', is located near one of the springs that issue along a line at the foot of the Greensand bench, no doubt influencing early decisions to build a settlement on these sites. To the west, both Ailwood and Woolgarston are recorded in the Domesday Book. Little Woolgarston, to the west lies on the route of an old road, much used by the stone industry, that ran northwards from Winspit and Worth Matravers, across the Purbeck Hills via the Rollington dry valley to Rollington itself, and along Thrasher's Lane to the little port on Wych Lake. Challow, the most westerly of these farms, inevitably takes its name from *cealc* and *weg* – chalk way. As a unit, this line of farms forms a magnificent belvedere, looking southwards across Purbeck's vale to the skyline of the quarries on the limestone plateau.

Purbeck Marble is not a true marble; rather its is a limestone rich in the shells of a small freshwater snail, *Viviparus,* that takes a ready polish and has been widely used in architecture, particularly in local churches and in Salisbury Cathedral. Hutchins wrote, in his seminal *History and Antiquities of Dorset*, 'At or near Dunshay was formerly dug marble of several colours, blue, red, spotted and grey, but chiefly the latter; all of a coarse sort. The grey is a congeries (an aggregation) of shells; vast quantities of it are found in our ancient churches.' The seams of Purbeck Marble outcrop on the east coast of Purbeck at Peveril Point (where they can be seen in the centre of the little dish-shaped outcrop of rocks) and continue westwards at the foot of the slope that leads up from the vale to the limestone plateau all the way to Worbarrow Tout. It was worked in quarries along this outcrop and then taken by cart across Corfe Common to the workshops in West Street, Corfe Castle. Old spoil heaps and abandoned quarries abound amongst the woods to the north of Langton Matravers and to the west as far as Blashenwell.

Corfe Common and the land of the marble farms.

The marble was worked at Combe just west of Swanage Middle School, to supply material for the rebuilding of the Temple church in London after the blitz, but the first of the marble farms is Wilkswood, to the north of Langton Matravers. Once the site of a priory, its abandoned marble pits are some of the oldest in Purbeck. Beyond Langton West Wood is the appropriately named Quarr Farm, now relatively modest buildings, but once the site of pits that supplied both marble, and another of Purbeck's building stones, burr, for use in Corfe Castle. If Godlingston Manor is the finest of the buildings in the northern line of settlement, Dunshay Manor to the west of Quarr is indubitably its equivalent among the marble farms. Incorporating the ancient 'longhouse', Dunshay today is something of a palimpsest of different styles and ages The manor house of today was rebuilt by John Dolling in 1642, but at a much earlier date Alice de Briwere, living on the same site, supplied 12,000 tons of marble for the building of Salisbury Cathedral. Mary Spencer Watson, the late incumbent of Dunshay Manor, carried on a long tradition, sculpting and carving in a wide variety of stone.

Blashenwell Farm.

Afflington, the next farm to the west, is recorded in the Domesday Book as *Alvronetone*, and was granted the right to hold a fair and market in the time of Henry III. It is perhaps the best example of a 'lost village' in the southern line of settlement, since at the end of the seventeenth century, between fifteen and twenty houses stood on the present site. Fifty people still lived there in 1800. Scoles Farm and Lynch Farm continue the line to the west. Blashenwell, nestling at the foot of the slopes that lead down from Kingston's woods, is the most westerly of the 'marble farms'. Recorded as *Blachenwelle* – spring or stream where cloth is bleached – in 956, the farm lies in one of Purbeck's most delightful spots. The spring to the south is dammed by a wall, providing a source of water for the huge waterwheel still in existence on the western wall of the farm buildings. The spring also supplies the attractive duck pond, neatly enclosed by a stone wall, to the north of the farm. A stream drains north from the pond across an area of calcareous tufa, deposited from the lime-rich water. The site is one of some antiquity, with a host of artefacts dating back to Mesolithic (Stone Age) times. In more recent times Blashenwell saw the working of Purbeck Marble, and spoil heaps and hollows marking old pits abound in the vicinity. Purbeck Marble was worked particularly in the 1870s for the new church of St James, up the hill in Kingston, where it is used to stunning effect in the chancel screen. So this series of half-hidden, isolated farms marks the line of busy mediaeval industrial activity, long since ceased, but leaving an indelible mark on the landscape of the vale.

The western vale around Blashenwell.

To the west of Corfe Castle a different landscape appears in the vale. No busy main road thrusts its way through the valley; whistles of steam engines are only a distant echo from the valley to the east. Somnolent Church Knowle, high on its bench under Knowle Hill, now bereft of village store and post office, but retaining a busy pub, is the only focus of settlement. Farms are again strung out in two lines in the north and south of the vale. In the north the easternmost farm is Glebe, just west of Corfe and the line continues to Manor Farm at Steeple. The southern farms nestle under the slopes up to the windswept limestone plateau in the lee of Smedmore Hill, from East Orchard to the magnificent Bradle in the west. Beyond Steeple Leaze, the last inhabited farm in the valley, lie the forbidden lands of the ranges. Here the farms are derelict and silent, Tyneham village is half restored but still heavy with poignant memories, but sheep and cattle still munch and chew their way across the damp pastures of westernmost Purbeck.

After passing the unpretentious Glebe, the first of the northern line of farms that claims attention is Bucknowle. There appears to be a long history of settlement on this gravel-capped knoll just to the west of Corfe Common – one of the few relatively dry sites in the centre of the vale. In the late twentieth century, between 1976 and 1991, the

Bucknowle House.

evidence for the existence of Roman villa on the site was gradually uncovered. The discovery of Roman pottery led to further excavations in which a tessellated pavement was found, together with Roman coins. Thus was discovered the first Roman villa south of the Chalk ridge on a sunny south-facing dry site in the vale; probably one of the best in its western part, which was still quite wooded at the time. Bucknowle was certainly a Saxon estate: *Chenolle* was recorded as one of nine manors in the present parish of Church Knowle, and similar names are recorded regularly from 1285, with *Bucknoll* – 'hill top belonging to a man called Bubba' (from the original *Bubecnolle*) – appearing in 1584. Other records in the late seventeenth century and the early eighteenth century indicate sizeable farms here. Today there are two main groups of buildings on the gravel knoll. Bucknowle House, best seen from the western end of Corfe Common, is a large Victorian building, built in Tudor style. West Bucknowle is early Victorian in age, and seems to have been built on the site of another earlier house that had been burnt down.

Barely a half mile to the west of Church Knowle itself is Barnston Manor, said to be the oldest continuously inhabited building in Purbeck. Once again the site, south-facing and on the higher slopes of the Wealden Beds, was one of the original Saxon estates, as appears in the Domesday Book, and is mentioned in 1375 as *Barneston* – a farm belonging to a man called Beorn. Barnston Manor itself seems to date from

The western vale in snow.

The western vale from Knowle Hill.

approximately 1280, built by a member of the Estoke family. Later additions and alterations have contributed to the appeal of one of the finest country houses in Purbeck. It remained as a farmhouse for a long period of time, but in the 1970s it was leased for the production of a number of theatrical performances. Farm buildings on the road were a more recent addition. Whiteway Farm, to the west suggests a location on an ancient trackway over the Purbeck Chalk ridge to the north. The remains of an older mediaeval settlement remain – *Wyteweye* is first mentioned in 1284, with the present farmhouse probably dating from 1600.

Barnston Manor.

Blackmanston Farm lies in the next parish to the west, Steeple. Evidence for the existence of the Domesday settlement is found on either side of the Corfe River to the south of the Elizabethan manor house which houses today's farm. Steeple Manor House, Manor Farm and the parish church of Steeple lie just off the road that soon begins to rise up the southern face of the Purbeck Hills. The tiny cluster of buildings with a church suggests that the site was once more heavily populated. The church itself dates from the twelfth century, with later additions. A fourteenth century marriage between the Lawrence and Washington families is marked by the coats of arms of the two families on a carved tablet. John Washington emigrated to America, and his great – grandson George became the first President of the United States, and the stars and stripes emblem has its origins in the Washington coat of arms displayed in the church. Steeple Leaze Farm, overlooking the little trickle that is the infant Corfe River, is the most westerly inhabited farm in the vale. Although the present farm holding is relatively modest, the present incumbent farms much of the land within the range lands to the west. Thus many of the fields and pastures to the west have a bright well-kept appearance and are part of the flourishing farming community of the western vale.

Blackmanston Farm.

The southern line of settlement in the western vale seems to have originated in a group of Saxon estates, similar to the one on the northern side of the vale. The three main farms, East and West Orchard and Bradle are all mentioned in the Domesday Book. Today, the first two are secretive little farms tucked away off the road that comes down from Barnston Cross roads and climbs up the limestone slopes to overlook the Kimmeridge lowland. The orchard, hardly of note today, was mentioned in Domesday Book itself. Bradle, to the west, much grander by far, appears in Domeday Book as *Bradelege* 'broad wood or clearing' suggesting that it may well have been one of the earlier clearances in the woodland that would have covered much of the central vale. With its huge chimneys, Bradle is one of the finest examples of farm architecture in Purbeck. Tiny Puddle Mill Farm, on the banks of the Corfe or Wicken, is probably much later, the result of enclosure of grazing lands on either bank of the river.

Steeple church.

Steeple village and the western vale.

The little road that leaves the main ridge-top road in West Purbeck descends steeply through an oak and ash copse to enter the now forbidden vale. Most of the fields on either side are generally well cared for, even though the ruined North Egliston is a reminder of a more fortunate past. The road crosses the watershed between the Corfe River and the Tyneham brook, and the most westerly part of the vale, with Worbarrow Bay and distant Portland as a backdrop, is suddenly revealed. On the slopes to the left is Tyneham Great Wood, hiding what remains of Tyneham House, once the home of the Bonds of Tyneham. There is at once a mystery and a sadness about the now tangled and unmanaged dank woods of the Tyneham gwyle and the slopes that sweep up to the landward side of Gad Cliff to the south and the Chalk ridge to the north. At first sight this might seem to be a landscape of dereliction and abandonment, the result of a heavy military presence.

The western vale looking east from near Bradle Farm.

Although Tyneham remains a deserted village since the population was required to leave by the Army in 1943, there is an air of tranquillity and meaningful change about the Tyneham vale now. More buildings are being restored, new walks and footpaths have been created, sheep and cattle managed from Steeple Leaze have a legitimate and almost permanent presence in the fields. It is true that a scrub of thistle, ragwort and gorse still clothes several of the fields, that numbered targets still disfigure the slopes leading to Gad Cliff and Worbarrow Tout, and that visitors are still hemmed in by fences with warning signs denying access to areas beyond the paths. A positive view suggests that the Army presence has helped to preserve the unique ecology of the vale and protect the Tyneham lowland from some of the worst depredations that tourism has brought to beauty spots elsewhere on the coast. This is not a viewpoint that is shared by all: some say that Tyneham folk would never have allowed the inevitable damage that intensive tourism brings – that it would have been controlled in the same way that it is at Kimmeridge, with its modest car parks and the occasional ice cream van.

Tyneham village.

Man's presence in the Tyneham vale has a long history. Domesday Book records four Tynehams, but does not mention the outlying farms of North and South Egliston (the latter lies on the far side of the limestone ridge in the Kimmeridge lowland) or Baltington. It is generally agreed that the three outlying farms were almost certainly the other Tynehams. In Domesday times the sites would have been more than just farms – it is likely that they were thriving hamlets. The sites of Baltington and North Egliston include earthworks that mark house remains and their accompanying gardens. Mediaeval cultivation strips can be traced at these sites, all in harmony with the hedge-lines that still indicate the boundaries of the original holdings. Tyneham House, once a central feature in the farming landscape of the Tyneham vale, is now only a tragic vestige of its former self. The oldest part of the house was probably fourteenth century, but the main body of the building as it existed before the Second World War was Elizabethan. It changed ownership many times before it passed into the hands of the Bonds, the incumbents at the time of the evacuation of the valley in 1943, who kept it until 1952. Much of the stonework was removed in the late 1960s, although parts of the early-fourteenth-century hall still remain.

Today the village landscape of Tyneham is one of partial restoration and continuing dereliction. The church of St Mary is now the centrepiece of attraction for visitors. Although parts date back to mediaeval times, much of the fabric of the building was added at a later date. The church is now within the benefice of the Corfe Valley churches, administered by the Rector from Corfe Castle. Services are now held several times during the year, including the poignant one on Remembrance Sunday in November. The old school has also been restored, with a classroom scene reminiscing on rural education in a perhaps innocent age now lost forever. Post Office Row, with its four cottages, and the former focus of the village, has been tidied, with the ancient telephone kiosk a reminder of the time when outside communication first became possible in Tyneham. The sturdy Rectory, much damaged by a fire in the 1960s, is now part of the Tyneham trail that embraces several other buildings that were all essential elements in village life, including the two most recent restorations, Double Cottages and Gardener's Cottage.

St Mary's, Tyneham.

Tyneham is unique in Dorset, if not in southern England. As the villagers left in 1943, they pinned a notice on the door of the church. It read simply – 'Please treat the church and houses with care… we shall return one day, and thank you for treating the village kindly'. Sadly the Army did not keep its promise and they never did return, although it has often been said that a number did not want to anyway. Although the public is allowed access to Tyneham on weekends and during the main holidays of the year, the Tyneham vale looks destined at the moment to remain uninhabited for the foreseeable future. Perhaps Tyneham village was not meant to survive into the twenty-first century – better it should remain as a permanent memorial to rural life in the vale in the early twentieth century

Chapter Six

Landscape of Stone

Purbeck's limestone lands stretch from Swanage in the east, where much of the southern half of the town is built on Purbeck limestones, to Gad Cliff and Worbarrow Tout in the west where the limestone dips steeply to leave only a narrow outcrop. Most of the limestone lands are underlain by the Purbeck limestones, except for an arc, underlain by Portland Limestone, that swings round from St Aldhelm's Head through the plateau country to the south of Kingston to the northern slopes of Smedmore Hill overlooking Kimmeridge in the west.

Seen from the Purbeck Hills to the north, the limestone lands are a bare, windswept plateau, whose large stone-enclosed fields contrast so sharply with the hedgerow-defined smaller fields of the vale – a contrast no better seen than in the west where the small fields to the west of Bradle give way to the great open enclosures, littered with sharp stone fragments, on the northern side of Smedmore Hill. The limestone lands are treeless too, apart from the plantations around Kingston and the bleak, aptly named, Polar Wood on the northern side of Swyre Head. Man's preoccupation with the working of the limestones underlying the plateau gives a different character to certain parts of the limestone lands. Just west of Swanage it is a land of overgrown spoil heaps, half-vegetated hollows, and abandoned stone workings. Around Langton and Acton is the heartland of stone working, with small quarries eating into the surface of the Purbeck Beds, and quarrymen's huts and enclosures seemingly one with the grey of the limestone beneath. Here the ancient Priest's Way, from Worth to Swanage, makes its meandering way across the open fields of the plateau. Beyond windswept Worth, the great unforgiving chasm of Swanworth cuts right through the surface Purbeck Beds to reveal the underlying Portland limestones, presenting an endless challenge of restoration in the years to come. In a sense, the landscape of stone is very much the landscape of quarrying, both past and present, from the hummocky, overgrown and abandoned workings to the west of Swanage to the open quarries in the west at Swanworth and at St Aldhelm's Head. An important difference is that in the east it is the Purbeck Beds that yield a whole variety of building stones, whist in the west it is the Portland Beds, or in quarryman's parlance, the Purbeck Portland Stone which is worked.

The limestone plateau near Acton.

Swanage's housing estates and bungalow developments give way quite abruptly to the old quarry lands of Townsend, which extended westwards to some of the farms, such as California and Belle Vue, that are still a sturdy and solid part of today's landscape.

Old quarry shaft near Anvil Point.

The Townsend quarries were at one time one of the most intensively worked areas of southern Purbeck, operating from 1700 to just before the Second World War; the workings extended to over 300 acres and until recently many of the entrances to the shafts were still visible These shafts were originally known as 'slides' since they were driven into the hillside at a low angle. The passages gave access to the most valued of the building stones in the Purbeck Beds. The Cinder Bed, full of oysters and of no value at all as a building stone, served as a marker. Above it, in descending order, were the Laning Vein, the Freestone Vein and the Downs Vein. Below the Cinder Bed was the New Vein. Each of the Veins consisted of a number of beds, most of which could be used for building purposes. Carts without wheels, basically sledges, could be drawn up the slides. With the introduction of cables, the slides could be driven deeper to tap different veins of stone. From each slide 'lanes' were driven off at intervals to allow access to the vein of stone that was being worked. The stone was loaded on to the carts and then drawn by the quarrymen to the slide. Here the carts were drawn up to the surface by a donkey, attached to a wooden arm or 'spack', attached to a capstan. Some of the workings, such as Cowlease, extended some 120 feet into the ground.

Old quarry workings at Townsend.

This great area of stone working was thus one of the busiest in Purbeck, with numerous slides and a labyrinthine network of lanes at depth. Potentially a major hazard to the dwellings above, the occasional disaster did occur, as in 1895 when one of the houses in Alexandra Terrace collapsed into one of the lanes extending out from the Cowlease working. Generally the lanes were well shored up, and many of the outer streets in south-west Swanage are still underlain by old workings. Planning permission has been refused where developers seek to build on the higher parts of the hillside as new properties would be particularly vulnerable.

Today different uses prevail on the site of the old Townsend workings. Immediately to the west of the roads that lead off Bon Accord Road in Swanage is the 32 acre Townsend Nature Reserve administered by the Dorset Wildlife Trust since 1978. This is an area of the original Townsend workings that is now a series of mounds and hollows, the latter concealing entrances to the 'slides'. Access to the former workings is no longer permitted for safety reasons and also because the old 'lanes' are now used by hibernating bats, including the rare greater horseshoe bat. The calcareous grassland of the reserve is particularly rich in wild flowers, including seven species of orchids.

Kidney vetch attracts an uncommon species, the small blue butterfly; the marbled white and common blue butterflies are quite common. There are some remains of the old *scar-heaps* and *spawls*, bright with Wild Thyme, Yellow-wort, Horseshoe-vetch and Lady's Bedstraw Much of the reserve is covered with scrub, mainly blackthorn and hawthorn, but also wild privet and brambles. Trees have gradually established themselves in the reserve and now shelter a rich and varied birdlife. Magpies and wood-pidgeons are common, and migrant birds such as redstarts and flycatchers pass through the reserve. Townsend is grazed by horses during parts of the year in order to keep the turf short and to discourage the spread of scrub. Thus a flowery sward is maintained and is not invaded by coarser species. Signboards are unobtrusive, and the atmosphere is one of calm relaxation, with the horses quietly browsing the sward of well-cropped grass, with hardly a hint of the immense activity of the original workings. With its splendid commanding views over Swanage Bay to the north, the reserve is one of the delights of the present day Swanage environment. One reminder of past industry is the most easterly of the quarries, one of the California Group, that still operates, tucked away into the hillside to the south of the Nature Reserve, working the same veins that attracted so much attention to the area in the nineteenth century.

California Quarry.

Beyond the Nature Reserve to the west, the former Townsend quarries have a more workaday use, with Swanage Household Waste site's reclaimed contours bringing a strange rounded uniformity to a landscape that has hitherto been much more broken with its spoil heaps and overgrown hollows. Another use of the former quarries is the extensive caravan site that now dominates much of the land between Swanage's bungalows and the open country to the south. A more open landscape prevails westwards towards the Langton parish boundary, with Belle Vue and Verney Farm reminding us of a more pastoral past that existed before the quarrymen moved into the area in the 1700s.

California Farm.

The Priest's Way, along which the minister from Worth used to travel to celebrate services in the tiny fishing village that is now Swanage, leads westwards from near Belle Vue farm, where it first becomes discernible after a half-disguised passage through suburban Swanage. It is the essential link between the brick and stone terraces of nineteenth century Swanage and the wide open windswept lands to the east of Worth Matravers. For most of its route it is lined with the inevitable stone walls, often much overgrown with blackthorn, bramble and hawthorn, which bring a measure of shelter and seclusion. Beyond Verney Farm it has an airy, open aspect – boundless open skies country, as nowhere else in Purbeck, conveying the very essence of these limestone lands of South Purbeck, best perhaps on a fine early spring day when the sun has a

The Priest's Way.

Notice concerning new quarrying.

new warmth, and the first green shoots have appeared in the hawthorns lining the way. Just inside Langton parish, alongside the way, the National Trust keeps an ancient limekiln in good repair. After the way has crossed the track leading from Durnford Drove in Langton to Spyway Barn and Dancing Ledge, the western horizon begins to herald a new contemporary quarrying landscape around the ancient settlement of Acton. Possibly the most celebrated of the quarries west of Acton is Keates Quarry. Here particularly large dinosaur footprints were discovered in the bottom bed of the Freestone Vein in the late 1990s. Notices along the way tell of the imminent exhaustion of stone, and plans for the opening up of new surface workings to the south in fields hitherto untouched by brightly coloured quarryman's excavator, revealing new rock faces that will yield stone for a twenty-first century industry that is so conservation conscious.

Acton, high on the windswept plateau above Langton Matravers, and linked to the Priest's Way to the south by a wide gravel track, is unique in Purbeck. In Domesday Book it was recorded as *Tacatone* – 'farm where young sheep are reared'. Farmhouse, farm labourers' cottages and the shepherd's cottage still remain but their use has changed. Acton's expansion came in the nineteenth century with the growth of the quarries around the settlement. Today it is still a quarrymen's settlement, but some of the solid stone houses are now holiday homes and others welcome commuters home in the evening. It is a dour, even introspective, place, quite separate from nearby Langton, although the centre of the settlement, almost courtyard-like, is a gem of this little hamlet. Beneath Acton the old workings of past quarry-mining can still be traced and some of its homes rest only on fifteen feet of stone above the lanes of the old workings. Time has changed Acton very little: few tourists visit the huddled cottages, service buses on the Langton to Kingston road rush past the end of the track to Acton and the only welcome visitor is the morning postal van. Acton is thus caught in something of a time warp, but is an essential link to the long-lost busy times of the heyday of mining on this open, treeless land to the west of Langton.

Quarry landscape west of Acton.

Westwards from Acton, as Langton Parish gives way to Worth, the plateau becomes even more open to the winds that rush in from the Channel to the south. Old quarry mines were very active in this area, and the surface remains of their workings are visible just off the road to the north. The few cottages that make up Gallows Gore (at one time Callos Gore (meaning a triangle of unproductive land) were built as Turnpike Cottages in the late eighteenth century and mark the site of the old crossroads here. To the south of the Langton to Worth road and just beyond the Priest's Way is Eastington Farm, now in National Trust ownership. Eastington was *Estinton* in 1209, simply 'farm to the east of the village'. It has a long and quite distinguished history, being a manor in the late mediaeval times to which a number of prominent local farms, such as Haycrafts and Little Kimmeridge belonged. It passed into the ownership of Christchurch Priory, and later into the hands of the Crown. It was then owned by Sir

Acton from the south.

Crundel Cottages, Acton.

Eastington Farm.

Swanworth Quarry.

Christopher Hatton, one time owner of Corfe Castle. The last private owners were the Bankes family, who bequeathed it to the National Trust in the early 1980s. Today the former seventeenth century farmhouse is solid, secure and shelters behind massive stone walls, bastions against the fierce gusts that storm in from the coast. Farther to the west is Seacombe House, with its observatory keeping Purbeck's own watch on the heavens, with some distinction. The view from Seacombe House down the valley towards the sea embraces more of the old mediaeval landscape of the strip lynchets. Beyond Worth village itself, the great gash of Swanworth Quarry cuts deeply into the limestone plateau. Originally known as Sheepsleights (derived from *slaeget* – a sheep's pasture), some suggest that the derivation is from'Ship's Lights' for from Swanworth there are fine views out to sea. The first workings appear to have been in the early twentieth century when Billy Brown and Buff Bowers produced stone setts for local use. Today's quarry began life as Worth Quarries in 1923, with its first major contract being to produce hard core for the new Valley Road between Corfe Castle and Coombe on the western outskirts of Swanage. This set a pattern of exploitation for the quarry. Within the huge site, one of the largest quarries in Dorset, the Purbeck Beds occupy the sides of the valley in which it is cut, and the Portland Beds lie below, with the lower part of the Portland Beds, the Portland Sand, forming the floor of the present quarry.

Unusually, the Portland Limestone here is not often of the quality to yield 'dimension stone' the high quality building stone that is used so widely in southern England and beyond. The production of dimension stone from the quarry is restricted to purely local contracts. Other uses have been found for the Purbeck Portland Stone, as it is known, in this quarry. At one time it had its own lime kilns to produce agricultural lime. With the bankruptcy of Worth Quarries in 1933, a new company, Swanworth Quarries was formed. Lime continued to be produced, but with a substitute coming on to the market it soon became obvious that the future of the quarry lay in the production of aggregate and hardcore, with important contracts including reclamation projects at Baiter and the Roll-On-Roll-Off ferry terminal in Poole.

At the beginning of the twenty-first century the end of quarrying at Swanworth is well in sight and the workings will close within the next few years. Today's talk is all of reclamation, and returning the valley to something resembling its former state, when its sides were rich in calcareous grassland flora and its accompanying wildlife. Restoration and re-contouring of the edges of the quarry should enable the original grassland to re-establish itself. New ponds will be created in the valley bottom and surrounded by wild flower meadows that will be newly planted with species such as Horseshoe-vetch, Cranesbill and Birdsfoot Trefoil, Tor Grass and Oat Grass to attract butterflies. Woodland will be re-established by planting a whole range of trees, including maple, ash, beech and oak, on the more sheltered slopes. Already extensive testing of seed mixtures on reclaimed slopes has shown which species are likely to survive best and produce appropriate plant associations for the re-landscaped valley. In a few years time when working has finally ceased, the valley will gradually return to form part of the natural pattern that drains down towards Chapman's Pool. Some reminders of its industrial past will remain, notably a series of carefully constructed exposures of the valley's geology for experts and students alike to study. Birdsong and the gentle drift of summer sea breezes through the new meadows will replace the the shrill of the siren, the deafening blast opening up a new face and the sonorous incessant rumble of quarry machinery.

Westwards, beyond Swanworth, the horizons of the plateau become wider, the wind more unrelenting, and the sea never far from view. A few cottages and bungalows straggle at the western limits of Worth village, and Renscombe Farm is the plateau's last farm east of the Kingston woods. Tucked away in the shelter of a slight hollow, it is recorded in Domesday book as *Romescombe*, and derives its name from Old English *hremn* and *cumb* 'Raven's valley'. The farm belonged to Cerne Abbey in mediaeval times, but passed to the crown on the dissolution of the monasteries and eventually to the Scott family of Enscombe. Much altered and enlarged, the farm still retains some attractive architectural features such as its door heads and stone mullioned windows.

St Aldhelm's Quarry.

St Aldhelm's Chapel.

Coastguard Cottages, St Aldhelm's Head.

The stone-wall fringed track, with its complementary thorn hedges, alongside the farm leads southwards to St Aldhelm's Quarry and eventually to St Aldhelm's Head. In St Aldhelm's Quarry, cut deeply into the side of the head of Pier Bottom, Purbeck Portland limestone is worked, with the Upper or Pond Freestone being the preferred horizon from which dimension stone is obtained. The Lower Freestone, which was so important as a source of dimension stone in the coastal quarries to the east is so thin as to be uneconomic. The quarry is still worked by the Haysom family: within the quarry a tall derrick crane is preserved, which once used to operate at Dancing Ledge Quarries. This is probably the most remote of the limestone land's quarries, but it carries an air of lively and purposeful activity about it, with newly found blocks of dimension stone under the quarry walls and carefully stacked dressed stone around the corrugated iron buildings that shelter from the winds that constantly funnel up Pier Bottom from Weymouth Bay. Leaving the quarry, the track continues, now between fences of barbed wire to St Aldhelm's Chapel, the coastguard watch station and the row of coastguard cottages. Built in 1834, the cottages, a real landmark throughout southern Purbeck, were used as a weaving centre in the mid-twentieth century, but are now just more holiday cottages, albeit those with probably the best view of all.

Deep valleys cut into the limestone lands westwards from the track, breaking up the continuity that it displays to the east. All of these valleys focus on Chapman's Pool, sufficiently deeply incised and wooded at their seaward ends to merit their being called 'gwyles' – a local Purbeck word for steep-sided wooded valley. Hill Bottom leads down from Swanworth Quarry, and picks up the little side valley that comes down from Renscombe Farm. Sheltered in a small combe on the northern side of Hill Bottom, just after it is joined by the Renscombe valley is the tiny hamlet of Hill Bottom, once used by smugglers perhaps. Passing through the tollgate into Corfe Castle parish the track leads into the more open valley of West Hill Bottom, with its delightfully situated cottages high on its western side, looking out to Chapman's Pool, St Aldhelm's Head and its race beyond.

On the opposite side of the valley, high on the slopes leading up to Kingston Down is one of the best preserved of ancient field systems in Purbeck. Best seen in the low rays of winter sunshine, the walls of the fields enclose plots that are almost rectangular. Downward movement of the soil has meant that the upper and lower walls of each plot are particularly well marked, almost lynchet-like in their clarity. Close examination of the site reveals evidence of an enclosure, round houses and storage pits.

Beyond West Hill Bottom the plateau takes on a different character, for planted woodland makes its first appearance. The silence of the woods of the Plantation, stretching

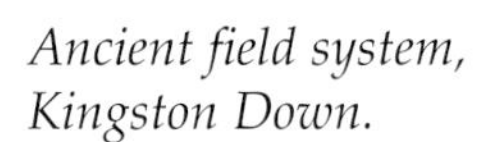
Ancient field system, Kingston Down.

from the road down to Chapman's Pool to the track leading to Encombe House is broken only by the shrill cries of pheasants. These woods half encircling Kingston have an almost claustrophobic effect on the village, seemingly blocking it off from the stunningly open landscape to the south. The woodland theme is continued on the slopes surrounding the Encombe lowland and the Golden Bowl: Quarry Wood extends westwards as far as the road leading down to Encombe from Kingston. Open land beyond carries the obelisk, raised in Seacombe-quarried Portland Stone, built in 1835 in memory of Lord Stowell, the first Earl of Eldon's elder brother. Westwards beyond the track that runs through fields, often planted with maize at the present time, is Purbeck's most enigmatic and exposed patch of woodland, Polar Wood. Crumbling stone walls afford little protection for the ash trees from the winter gales that lash Swyre Head and rush across the Golden Bowl to this curious extended rectangle of woodland that seems almost tired of its exposed and relentless battle against the elements. Spring brings a carpet of bluebells that add a brightness otherwise denied this hoary old patch of woodland. Across the broad acres of stone-walled fields to the north are two more exposed coppices – Newfoundland, and the smaller patch that shelters Orchard Hill Farm.

The Golden Bowl.

Smedmore Hill and majestic Swyre Head are the western arm of the Portland limestone plateau, looming hugely over the Kimmeridge lowland to the west. Great open fields, now mostly enclosed by barbed wire stretch across the dip slope of Smedmore Hill that reaches down towards Bradle Farm and the Vale of Purbeck.

Polar Wood.

The view westwards from Swyre Head.

Thickly scattered with limestone debris, difficult enough to plough and cultivate, these are some of Purbeck's largest cereal yielders. The continuity of these fields is broken by the strange, almost unexpected dry valley that runs down from above Bradle Farm to Bradle itself. Swyre is Purbeck's culminating height, just a few metres above Godlingston Hill overlooking the Ulwell gap. Its views are all embracing in every direction. Westwards the eye takes in the magnificent coastal seascape that stretches away to Portland on the western horizon from the more intimate details of the Kimmeridge lowland in the immediate foreground. Gad Cliff beyond leads away to Worbarrow Tout and the brilliant Chalk cliffs of the Lulworth coastline and distant White Nothe. Swinging round to the east, Smedmore's scarp slopes pass westwards to the Portland Stone ramparts that fringe Kimmeridge and its lowland to the north. Copse and pasture of the central vale are succeeded to the north by the long line of the Purbeck Hills, with glimpses beyond of heathland, Poole Harbour and the distant skylines of Dorset's downland and Cranborne Chase. Bastions of the distant Chalk such as Melbury Hill and Wiltshire's Win Green are just visible to the roving naked eye. Eastwards the Golden Bowl occupies the foreground, with Encombe nestling amidst its trees. Beyond the ridge leading out to Houns-tout, is St Aldhelm's Head, all bright limestone against the blue sea beyond Chapman's Pool ending the maritime curve running from Kimmeridge Bay. Purbeck's limestone lands can be seen in retrospect beyond Worth, and on a far distant horizon, the white Chalk cliffs of Scratchell's Bay in the Isle of Wight bring geological continuity to the Purbeck scene. Finally, those that stand on Swyre's lonely heights on a clear night may see a distant glow in the sky beyond the sea's horizon. Cherbourg's lights bring a human continuity across a gap of 90 kilometres (55 miles) and a remembered glimpse of lands across the Channel.

Chapter Seven

The Kimmeridge Lowland

Although the Kimmeridge Clay makes its first appearance at the base of St Aldhelm's Head, the lowland itself does not properly begin until the western slopes of Houns-tout are reached. Encombe House nestles in the eastern half of the lowland, which is almost separated from the larger western half by the inland promontory of Swyre Head. The main area of the lowland is dominated by the Portland Limestone escarpment that bounds it on the landward side. Treves describes the escarpment as… 'The downs here are in long rolling lines, like terrific sea combers about to break on a shoal.' The view of this lowland enclave, seen from the old quarry above the village, where the roads from Bradle and Steeple meet, is one of the most stunning in Purbeck. Framed by Smedmore Hill to the left and distant Tyneham Cap to the west, the lowland is smooth and undulating, with gentle hillocks such as Metherills, just beyond Kimmeridge village, rising gracefully in almost perfect curves above the shallow valleys of the tiny streams that drain down to the coast. The wide open fields to the west lap around the clumps of pines that stand almost sentinel-like beneath the steep surrounding slopes of the Portland Limestone. All of the lowland slopes towards

Smedmore Hill and Kimmeridge village.

The escarpment of Portland Limestone that surrounds the Kimmeridge Lowland.

The Golden Bowl.

the sea: much of it is fine pasture, but it is also some of the best-yielding cereal land in Purbeck, where maize has become increasingly important since the late twentieth century. On the horizon lies the long low profile of distant Portland, seemingly ever-present in the seascapes of this part of the Purbeck coast. This is rural Purbeck at its finest: change here has been slow. The red flags, the high fences and the hidden and ruined western farms such as South Egliston remind us of the Army presence that has sealed off the slopes leading up to Tyneham Cap for the foreseeable future.

Encombe appear to have a number of different meanings; for some it is simply 'great valley', for others its name derives from the thirteenth century *Hennecumbe* – 'valley of the water-hens' and last and most obviously 'end of the valley'. Encombe House is the centrepiece in the lowland encircled by the Portland Limestone escarpment which acts almost like a protective hand. The western part of the great open combe, under the shadow of Swyre Head, is referred to as the Golden Bowl, although this name is often used to encompass the whole of the lowland. Some woodland clings to the steep slopes of Swyre Head; at other places on the scarp patches of planted conifers appear, whilst in the bottom of the combe, woods conveniently named Long Wood, Little Wood and Big Wood diversify the landscape, producing a delightful mix of copse, pasture and nearer the sea, arable land. South Gwyle, a steeply incised little valley carries the Encombe stream through dense and tangled thickets to the sea at Freshwater Steps. Treves wrote

Encombe House.

The lake, Encombe.

'I am unable to speak of this valley, because, owing to the atrocious conduct of the "trippers", the road through it has been very properly closed by the owner.' He even goes so far as to quote another writer (C.G. Harper in *The Hardy Country* (1905)) 'Think of all of the beautiful road scenery you have ever seen or heard of, and you will not have seen or been told of anything more beautiful, in its especial kind of beauty, than this sequestered road down into Lord Eldon's retreat.'

Encombe House from the path to Houns-tout.

The manor of Encombe originally belonged to Shaftesbury Abbey until the Dissolution. After the first two owners were beheaded, it passed to the Cullifords, who built the first Encombe House in the seventeenth century. Later it passed to George Pitt, whose son rebuilt the original Culliford House, creating an imposing exterior of Purbeck Portland Stone. Another generation of Pitts then became owners but were forced to sell to John Scott, later to become Lord Eldon, in 1807. The house and estate remained in the Scott family until 2003, when the house and the valley and Chapman's Pool were sold to the McVeighs, although the Scotts still retain Kingston village and much of the remainder of the estate.The whole building sits elegantly in the great combe of Encombe. Its central block is slightly recessed and wings extend out from either side, although the eastern one is incomplete. Impressive Doric colonnades flank the central block, and a bold cornice, extending across the whole building has a powerful integrating effect. The house is complemented on the seaward side by two lakes surrounded by attractive ornamental woodland. Rockery Bridge built of local stone, spans the little stream that links the lakes. Beyond the second lake lies Encombe Dairy, the workaday buildings from which all of the surrounding land is farmed. Swyre Head and the long ridge running out to Houns-tout thus provide the exquisite setting for one of Dorset's most remote and sequestered country houses.

Encombe Dairy.

Beneath the heights of Swyre Head the land is tumbled and hummocky, the result of landsliding where the Portland Limestone and Sand overlie the unstable Kimmeridge Clay. There is little evidence of landsliding today, and most of the activity probably took place in periglacial times. Halfway between Swyre Head and the crumbling cliffs of Kimmeridge Clay is Eldon Seat, with wonderful views over the Encombe estate to the east. It was erected by the first Earl of Eldon's daughter so that her father could rest and contemplate as he surveyed his lands; beside is a memorial to his favourite dog, Pincher. Beyond Swyre Head the lowlands of the Golden Bowl open out into the Kimmeridge lowland proper. Two entries in the Domesday Book coincide with the present day parish of Kimmeridge; Cameric was the part in which Kimmeridge village is now situated, and to the east lies Cuneliz. The latter became known as Little Kimmeridge. Hutchins, in his *History of Dorset*, describes three farms or hamlets at

Swalland Farm.

Smedmore, Little Kimmeridge and Chaldecot. Today Chaldecot is almost certainly Swalland Farm, and Little Kimmeridge survived as a single building until recently, about half a mile to the south of Smedmore.

Smedmore House itself is largely screened by trees planted to give shelter from the relentless winds that pour across Weymouth Bay. From the house the sea is only visible through a gap in the trees deliberately cut so that there was a view of the waters of Weymouth Bay. The outlook to the north-west is much more open, with the vista embracing Kimmeridge village with a backdrop of the magnificent Portland Limestone escarpment that runs away to distant Tyneham Cap.The nucleus of the present house, was known as the 'little Newe House', and was built by Sir William Clavell , in the early seventeenth century, when he moved from Barnston Manor in the Vale of Purbeck to be near his alum works at Kimmeridge Bay. The south-west garden front of the house was added by Edward Clavell in about 1700. The north-west front, seen by all those who travel down to Kimmeridge village and the sea, was added in 1761 by George Clavell. The Smedmore estate passed from the Clavells to the present owners, the Mansels, in the nineteenth century. Although perhaps lacking the dramatic surroundings of Encombe House, Smedmore rests easily in the lands of Kimmeridge, bringing a touch of architectural distinction to the open rolling fields of the lowland.

Smedmore House.

Swinging round behind the lands of Kimmeridge is the limestone escarpment of Smedmore Hill and its long extension westwards to Tyneham Cap. On Smedmore Hill itself there is evidence of mediaeval strip cultivation, which differs from that at Winspit

The lands of Cameric, west of Kimmeridge.

View looking towards the sea west of Kimmeridge village.

and Seacombe in that the strips run at right angles to the contours. Ploughing of these strips would have required extra expenditure of effort moving up and down the steep slopes of Smedmore, a degree of labour for which there is no obvious explanation. A walk from the old disused quarry in Portland Limestone above Kimmeridge village westwards to the Range boundary reveals the subtle changes in the landscape from Cuneliz to Cameric. Cuneliz is very much estate country, dominated by Smedmore itself and ancient Chaldecot, now the site of Swalland. Cameric has the homely line of thatched cottages that is Kimmeridge village, and beyond, the great open fields, usually given over to crops of wheat or maize, and farther still to the west the forbidden lands of the Lulworth Ranges, still happily grazed by sheep from Steeple Leaze Farm for most of the time. Across these lands drifts the smell of seaweed newly exposed on the ledges of Kimmeridge Bay, and nearer the bay the slightly sulphurous odour comes from the shales in the cliffs themselves. However, the undoubted polluting effects of Kimmeridge's industrial past, when enterprise succeeded enterprise around the bay, are now gone for ever, and the whole of this lowland has a endearingly pleasant somnolence about it that is another of Purbeck's unforeseen delights.

The Kimmeridge Lowland and Kimmeridge Bay.

Chapter Eight

The Village Landscape

The villages of Purbeck sit cosily in the rural landscapes that have nurtured and supported them over many centuries. Village landscapes reflect a number of elements that combine to produce the face of the village as we see it today. The village street plan, evolved over many hundreds of years, gives the clear outline of the village, whether it be somewhat amorphous such as at Studland, or tightly nucleated as at Worth Matravers, or spread along one arterial street such as at Langton Matravers. A second element in the village landscape are the buildings themselves. Cottage, stone terrace and more presumptious and elaborate villa, standing in its own spacious grounds, combine to give a felicitous mix in most of Purbeck's villages. Farm buildings add their own sturdy presence on the outskirts of Worth Matravers and Studland and occupy a more central and focal position as in Langton and Kimmeridge. In a deeply rural area such as Purbeck, industrial buildings contribute relatively little to the village landscape, even though Kingston's old rope factory did occupy a fairly central position in the village. Civic buildings, such as Corfe Castle's Town Hall and Kingston's one-time Reading Room add their own particular character to the village scene. The central position of the church acts as a key focus in nearly all of the villages, with the possible exception of Studland, where the church of St Nicholas is tucked away in the fields away from the central meeting place of the roads of the village.

Purbeck Stone cottages, Corfe Castle.

Building materials give essential character to a village, and everywhere in Purbeck its own rich heritage of stone is reflected in the villages, whether they sit on the outcrop of the limestone plateau as in the case of Kingston, or on outcrops of clay such as Kimmeridge and Church Knowle. Farther to the north, beyond the ridge of the Purbeck Hills, the heathstone from the heaths finds its way into cottage and church, and even the almost alien bricks are used in Studland and occasionally in Corfe Castle village, as in the upper storey of the Town Hall. Chalk and flint feature little in the buildings near the ridge of the Purbeck Hills simply because both are so broken by the violent earth movements that tilted the Chalk on its ends throughout Purbeck. In Kimmeridge thatch tends to dominate as the roofing material in the main street, and appears occasionally in Corfe's two main streets, whilst in the stone villages on the plateau, tiles cut from the thinner horizons in the Purbeck Beds are almost ubiquitous. Villages are distributed somewhat unevenly through Purbeck. The vast expanses of the heathlands muster four villages, all tucked away towards the edge of heath, valley bog and pine plantation. East Holme hides away on the edge of the Frome flood plain. Stoborough straggles southwards from the damp flood plain of the Frome, but lies within Arne parish. Arne itself lies away to the east, half-hidden and remote amidst the pine-clad gravel plateaux that overlook Poole Harbour: Studland is perhaps more seaside village than heathland settlement, yet only the grounds of a few Victorian villas open directly on to the sea. Many of its houses enjoy views that combine open heath with the distant blue waters of Poole Bay. Present day settlement avoids the open and windswept ridge of the Purbeck Hills, although in the past Purbeck's ancient peoples found it useful for burying their dead or building defensive settlements as at Flower's Barrow. In the Vale of Purbeck four villages lie within the patchwork of field and copse, together with the newcomer, Harman's Cross, hardly a village for some, but with enough life and vibrant functions to merit the name. Corfe Castle, Purbeck's largest village, thrusts southwards from the castle entrance towards the common and even merits the status of town in some opinions – indeed it has its old Town Hall and boasts a range of service functions seldom seen elsewhere in village Dorset. Westwards, Church Knowle is somnolent village Dorset at its most benign; Steeple with church and Manor House could only claim village status through being the centre of its parish and half derelict and ruined Tyneham, lost in the deep rurality of western Purbeck, slumbers on, awakening briefly on weekends and in the holidays.

East Holme: heathstone used for building St John's church.

On the limestone lands of the south, three villages offer sharp contrasts in site and form. Langton Matravers straggles lengthily for nearly one and a half kilometres (one mile) from Coombe to the open lands approaching Acton; Worth Matravers snugs into its shallow hollow around its duck pond and church, and Kingston, high above the western Vale, enjoys the status of Purbeck's one true hill village, reached from Corfe Castle only by two hair-pin bends. Kimmeridge lies remote and quiet in its own limestone-girt lowland.

St Nicholas's church, Arne.

East Holme is a mere handful of cottages, together with Holme Priory, an elegant eighteenth century country house, built on the site of a former Priory, and the nineteenth century church of St John, which was erected by Nathaniel Bond, in memory of his brother Denis. It has heathstone walls (probably quarried on the estate), with dressings of Ham Hill Stone. Some of the stones were retrieved from the old Priory. In the interior the arches were built of Bath and Ham Hill stone, with additional shafts using Purbeck Marble: Purbeck Stone tiles are used to good effect in the roof.

Stoborough, *Stanberge* in Domesday Book, originally 'stony barrow' (referring to King's Barrow just to the west of the main village), sits comfortably on the edge of its own heath. It is the main settlement in Arne parish, with Ridge's houses, small developments set amidst older houses within their own leafy grounds, lying halfway between Stoborough and the small cluster of buildings and church that is Arne. Stoborough is a functional sort of place with busy school and garage, and the half-thatched King's Arms forming a focus for the village. Sadly, a fourth element in this small service complex, the Stoborough Post Office and stores has recently closed – with the Post Office relocating in the garage. Traffic southward bound for the heart of Purbeck seldom stops in Stoborough, and the place has a commuter and retirement feel about it. A curiosity is the strangely named Melancholy Lane, branching off from busy Corfe Road, hinting perhaps at some sad, gloomy or sinister past, a marked contrast with the bright colours and individual designs of the Stoborough Meadows development.

Stoborough Heath.

The flat-topped heights of the Arne Peninsula, projecting out into the still waters of Poole Harbour are one of the landmarks of the Purbeck heathlands with their outline sharply reinforced by the spread of dark pine trees. Slightly to the east, in the shadow of the Arne heights is all that remains of a once busy village, where forty people lived in 1851 in the buildings clustered round the farm, the church and the school. Forty-three people lived in the hamlet of Slepe , on the road to Corfe, at the same time: today only the farm, occupied by English Nature and one other substantial house remain. Another small settlement existed at Coombe, close to the waters of Middlebere Lake- home for fifteen people in the mid-nineteenth century. Shipstal Point, where today the dusty grey-white path from Arne village reaches the sheltered waters of Wych Channel between the Arne Peninsula and Long Island, also had its cluster of cottages. There has been a massive and debilitating loss of population from the Arne settlements, a consequence of the difficulties of farming unrewarding soils and the promise of an easier life elsewhere.

The Toy Museum, Arne.

Today visitors come to the RSPB car park close to the village, and trudge down to Shipstal Point to enjoy the stunning views across Poole Harbour and its southern indented shores and the distant Purbeck Hills, or perhaps sit patiently in one of the hides in the RSPB Reserve, watching the abundant bird life of the saltmarsh and heathland. They might also visit the little church of St Nicholas, again, like St John at East Holme, built of the dark brown, heathstone, surprisingly warm in hue. Built in the thirteenth century, St Nicholas remains substantially unaltered, with its remarkable chancel and nave still retained as a single unit, which gives the interior a simple rustic charm. In the seventeenth century the roof was renewed and a bell gallery was added. Fortunately St Nicholas escaped the notorious Victorian restoration and remains one of the heathland's most attractive buildings, and Arne's most obvious treasure. People also visit Arne for its Toy Museum, housed in the Keeper's Cottage opposite the RSPB car park It is only the RSPB Reserve and the Toy Museum that bring visitors to this remote and quiet pine-darkened heathland village, one of Purbeck's hidden gems.

Frederick Treves' early twentieth century description of Studland is an admirable summary of the character of the village and is still relevant nearly a hundred years later 'It is a medley of country lanes, lost among trees, with a few thatched cottages dotted about in a wild garden of brambles, fern and gorse. There is nothing methodical or regular about Studland. There is no definite hamlet, no village street, no centre, no beginning, no end. It is merely a casual, unarranged sample of rural Dorset, brought in all its luxuriant greenness to the very water's edge.' Studland is first referred to as *Stollant* in Domeday Book: later derivations suggest 'a tract of land where a herd of horses is kept'.

'Amongst the myrtles and the fuchsias', Vine Cottage, Studland.

Using Treves' description one can attempt to identify the village of the early twenty-first century. Although the road from Swanage to the ferry at South Haven Point runs through Studland, the country lanes of Treves' day still meander between Ferry Road and the sea and busy weekends see traffic finding them difficult to negotiate on the way to Studland's three beaches. Thatched cottages, part Purbeck Stone, part heathstone, still hide behind hedgerow and trees in the lanes that lead down to Middle Beach and South Beach. Along Ferry Road and Swanage Road stone villas and brick terraces suggest something of a break with the past as do the brick and tile residences of Heath Green Road. Agglestone Road, a hidden cul-de-sac would have pleased Treves, for here a variety of houses styles look unobtrusively across the immediate heath to Little Sea, Studland Bay and distant Sandbanks and Bournemouth lying atop the cliffs of Poole Bay. Hotels and The Bankes Arms make up the mix of buildings that is Studland, and there is still an element of truth in Treves' comment that Studland 'turns its face from the sea to bury it among its myrtles and fuchsia bushes.'

Like Treves, it is difficult to find a hamlet, for today's Studland is a series of clusters, the most obvious of which is the one where lanes from the sea open on to Ferry Road and village hall and post office face one another across the busy road. Here it possible to differ from Treves, since this is a centre for both visitors and inhabitants alike. 'No beginning and no end' wrote Treves. Coming into Studland along the

Swanage Road, emerging from the shady pines of Woodhouse Hill, the visitor is greeted by modern stone villas that lead to the centre, but along Ferry Road substantial and imposing residences hide behind lines of high trees, and after the Knoll House Hotel, Studland just trickles away into the damp and dense birch and sallow thickets on the edge of Studland Heath. Apart and alien, the Glebeland Estate was unknown to Treves. Although the Bankes family had controlled development in Studland for much of the second half of the nineteenth century, they failed to control the sale of the glebeland after the First World War, when Bankes' agent failed to buy it after a missed train, and it fell into the hands of developers. Today it is still something of a scar, but growing shrubs and trees hide its intrusion on to the northern slopes of Ballard Down.

St Nicholas's church, Studland.

The Bankes family were the first to encourage the development of Studland as a holiday destination in the late nineteenth century. Friends began to frequent Studland, and by the beginning of the twentieth century it was beginning to be well known in fashionable London circles. Well-known names bought or rented properties in Studland and its reputation as a genteel resort began to grow. In 1926 the chain ferry began operating across the entrance to Poole Harbour, and Studland was soon accessible to the inhabitants and holiday makers from Bournemouth and Sandbanks. Buses began the run from Bournemouth to Swanage along tarmacked roads that replaced the old chalk tracks.

George Bankes rebuilt Studland Manor House in 1848, and it remained a private residence until the onset of the Second World War: later it became one of Studland's hotels, with fine lawns running down to the edge of the cliffs overlooking Redend Point and South Beach. Knoll House, in its pine-surrounded imposing setting overlooking Knoll Beach was built by one of the Bankes family, although it passed to the Duke of Hamilton in 1905: it was later rented by Maynard Keynes, and it opened as a hotel in 1930, and it has now been run by the Ferguson family since 1959.

If one building links today's Studland village landscape to its more distant past it is its splendid Norman church, tucked away in semi-seclusion at the end of Church Road. At the entrance to Church Road is the superbly worked village cross, carved from Purbeck-Portland Stone in the mid 1970s. Pitfield describes the church as 'the oldest surviving complete church in Dorset'. He suggests that it was probably a minster church in the eleventh and twelfth centuries, serving that part of Purbeck known as the Domesday hundred of Aylswood. Its origin is almost certainly Saxon, built just before the Norman conquest. It was extensively remodelled in the next two centuries, the nave in the late

Corfe Castle village.

eleventh century and the tower and chancel in the twelfth century. The interior of the church has an impressive and exquisite Norman character, particularly the arches and vaulting at the eastern end. Externally the corbel tables under the eaves have carvings of both human and animal heads. The tower was never completed as planned owing to the instability of the structures underneath, and it was finished by the present low gabled roof. By the late nineteenth century the whole building had become unstable. Strengthening of the existing fabric was skilfully carried out so that the Norman structure essentially survives. Well over a hundred years later the 1881 repairs are still effective in preserving the building and it remains the undoubted gem of Studland parish.

The Greyhound, Corfe Castle.

Although Corfe Castle is very much a feature of the Chalk ridge of the Purbeck Hills, the village is built mostly on the sands and clays of the Wealden Beds to the south, and can thus be regarded as a village of the Vale of Purbeck, owing its origin and status to the castle on the mound between the River Corfe and the Byle Brook. The castle was built in the eleventh century, but it seems unlikely that the village began to grow much before the twelfth century and it functioned as a small service centre for the castle itself, housing all of the tradesmen and servants who worked in the castle. It was granted a weekly market and an annual fair in 1212 by King John, and these rights were confirmed by Queen Elizabeth in 1559, when a second annual fair was also granted: the market was abandoned in the seventeenth century. As a small borough Corfe was given the right to send two MPs to Parliament in 1571, and this representation continued until 1832 when the Rotten Borough lost its two MPs as a result of the passing of the Great Reform Bill.

The Town House, Corfe Castle.

Corfe Castle is probably the largest and the most vibrant of all of Purbeck's villages. Although the village lies at the foot of the castle, it has a separate life that is entirely its own. Of all of Purbeck's villages it has perhaps the most obvious focus – the Square, overlooked by both church to the south and the castle to the north. It still retains the market cross, together with its water pump, said to be located on the site of a well in which the body of Edward the Martyr was hidden after he had been murdered in 978. Although the cross was destroyed in the sixteenth century, the base survived and a new cross was erected in 1897.

Around the Square are gathered the essentials of village life, General Stores, Post Office, baker, the Sweet Shop, and two pubs – The Greyhound and The Bankes Arms. In addition there are the more tourist-orientated National Trust shop, ice-cream parlour and a mineral and fossil shop. Even for a village that has such a high visitor count, this is service provision on a scale that is the envy of most Dorset villages.

Two buildings dominate the Square, The Greyhound Hotel on the north side and the Town House on the south side. The Greyhound Hotel partly extends above the footway as a 'jetty' built in 1733: the main part of the hotel was an old coaching station on the route between Wareham and Swanage in the eighteenth century. It includes two seventeenth century houses, both of which had jetties although the eastern one has now been blocked up, but one of its stone supporting pillars survives. The magnificent Town House was built in the eighteenth century, with the large robing room its outstanding feature. Its remarkable window is the dominant feature of the front of the house facing the Square, although its entrance is still from the churchyard at the rear. The Mayor and Barons robed here before proceeding to the Church for prayers. Today the lower part of the Town House is occupied by the village Post Office.

Furzeman's House.

Two streets extend away from the Square towards the common. East Street carries the main road to Swanage, whilst West Street gives more direct access to the common with a narrow tarmacked road leading away southwards to Blashenwell Farm in the shadow of the limestone lands to the south. West Street was formerly the main street in Corfe, clearly aligned with the entrance to the castle and the Square.

Penny's Cottages.

Tracks originally converged on the point where the present West Street meets the common, and it was along these tracks that Purbeck Marble was brought to be worked in West Street. Here it was stacked in 'bankers' and worked in the trimming shops: legend has it that over the years the marble accumulated so that some of the present houses are built on 12 feet of chippings. West Street is one of the finest village landscapes in Dorset with stone and tiled cottages lining the street in perfect harmony with the larger buildings such as the Town Hall. This is one of the smallest in the country, even rivalling the tiny structure at Newtown in the Isle of Wight. Corfe's Town Hall, built in 1774 on the site of a former town hall, is two-storeyed, the ground floor being built of Purbeck stone, the upper of bricks. The ground floor, which now houses Corfe's Museum, was originally the Town Prison, and the upper floor was the Council Chamber. Southwards Corfe's Post Office occupied a building over four hundred years old, before it moved to the Square in the 1990s. This building functioned as a Post Office even before there was an official postal service in 1840. Now it is a private dwelling. Almost opposite the Town Hall is the Fox Inn, one of the oldest alehouses in the village, of eighteenth century origin. It is small and has an exceptionally narrow front. It has been extended backwards at least three times. It has traditional links with the Ancient Order of Purbeck Marblers and Stonecutters.

Southwards other attractive sixteenth and seventeenth century cottages line the street, and on the corner is the old bakery. This building has the distinction of still possessing part of an Elizabethan timber framed wall, although most of the front of the building was rebuilt in the seventeenth century. In one of the rooms there is a fifteenth century fireplace, which may have come from the castle or a previous house on the same site. Behind the building there was a bakehouse for this house which was the site of Corfe's bakery until 1988. The village bakery re-opened in the Square in the 1990s. Farther on towards the common other buildings of note are Wayfaring Cottage and Furzeman's House, the latter dating from the seventeenth century: it was owned by Anthony Furzeman who was mayor of Corfe in 1659 and 1670. An interesting infill development is Penny's Cottages, Corfe's first cottages of the twenty-first century, which strike a happy blend with the existing village scene. Contrasting well with these modern dwellings is the row of stone cottages on the opposite side of the street, which were built for workers in the clay industry in the nineteenth century.

The Town Hall, Corfe Castle.

East Street, now Corfe's principal thoroughfare, first developed its importance in coaching days, when the turnpike was opened to Swanage in the mid 1760s. The marshy land adjacent to the common had to be drained and filled in and a new road built across the common to lead to Kingston and eventually to Swanage. Although East Street lacks the quiet rural repose of the cottages of West Street, its buildings contribute a different element to the village landscape. Cleall's Stores is a well-stocked Victorian shop and immediately next to it is another eighteenth century jetty protruding out from the main line of buildings. Seventeenth and eighteenth century cottages line the street southwards and include the Old Curatage, where Corfe's curate lived in the days when the Rector could afford such assistance, and the mediaeval Old Forge, the only building of this age to have survived in the village. Now it houses a small shop selling wrought iron pieces and other attractive gifts.

Morton's House, Corfe Castle.

Opposite the Old Forge Morton's House, now a comfortable and well-appointed hotel, is Corfe village's largest building. It was originally known as Daccombes, built for William Daccombe, a wealthy local landowner who died in 1599. It is said that its groundplan in the shape of a letter E was in honour of Queen Elizabeth I. In the early eighteenth century the house was sold to John Morton, and later passed to the Bond family of Creech. Before it achieved its present status as one of Purbeck's leading hotels it was divided into apartments in the nineteenth century. Beyond some attractive thatched cottages, and almost opposite the designer jewellers Y on the western side of the street, is the Old Cemetery, with the War Memorial of 1922 at its entrance, with the immortal words of William Barnes 'Dorset men don't shame their kind'. Past the entrance to the present Rectory is the First School, where children from throughout the Corfe valley are taught: originally it was the Bankes Memorial School, built in 1895.

Almost exactly opposite is the original school, built in 1834, the first purpose-built school in the Isle of Purbeck. It had two classrooms, the upstairs one for the older pupils. Today the building is the British Legion Club.

The Old School, Corfe Castle.

Next to the First School are the Almshouses, restored and renamed Jubilee House in 1977 and beyond the road to the School Playing Fields is the nineteenth century Castle Inn. Opposite the inn are Abbots Cottages, one of several affordable housing initiatives in the village – a welcome addition to a housing stock that is financially increasingly out of reach for many. Other eighteenth and nineteenth century cottages line East Street before there is a reminder of Corfe's past as a farming community – the Town Pound, where stray animals or those found on pasture to which they had no formal right, were impounded. Adjacent is the fine Pound Barn, recently rebuilt, facing the former nineteenth century Methodist church, now converted into private dwellings.

Corfe's parish church of St Edward The Martyr dominates the Square from the south in a manner that seems entirely fitting. A large church was first built in the thirteenth century to serve the religious needs of a growing community associated with the Castle. Over the centuries the fabric of the church deteriorated badly, and the whole building, with the exception of the fifteenth-century tower, was demolished and rebuilt in the Gothic style in 1859-60. Corfe's other church, the Congregational church, unlike the dominant parish church, hides away along an alleyway from East Street. It was built as an Independent chapel in 1835, with the original railings and arched lamp-bracket still remaining. Today the church has a delightful, well maintained garden between the alleyway and the Minister's House.

St Edward's church, Corfe Castle.

Corfe's much cherished open space, the Halves, lies between East Street and West Street. Originally The Halves were cultivated by Corfe's inhabitants as strip fields on the outskirts of the village. There were once three groups of open strip fields known as Almshouse, Middle and West Hawes on three sides of the village. Although the original strip boundaries are just visible they are used today to pasture horses, and cattle, and the whole green space of the Middle Hawes is now known as the Halves. From the Halves there are magnificent vistas, westwards to the Corfe valley and its backdrop of the western Purbeck Hills, and Creech Barrow, and northwards to the village and the Castle.

Corfe's railway station completes the village landscape. In the nineteenth century, in the heyday of the railway, the village station was a real asset to the village. Corfe's station, with its backdrop of the Castle and the gaps in the Purbeck Hills, is one of the most photogenic in England. Built of Purbeck stone and roofed with red tiles, it first opened in 1885.

In the inter-war years, when the private car brought few to Corfe, it was the main point of access for the village, and the rest of the Corfe valley. It survived closure in 1972, escaping demolition, and for a time housed a small business. It re-opened in 1995, and now is a busy station on the resurgent Swanage Railway. Bright fires warm it on cold winter days, and special trains serve it until late on balmy summer evenings. Complete with museum in the old goods' yard, it is an important focus of visitor life in the village, and no doubt it looks forward to the possible glory days of connection to the national network.

The Old Rectory, Church Knowle.

Harman's Cross, a mile or so to the east of Corfe, is a latecomer to the rural scene, probably originating in the nineteenth century. Built on one of the sandstone ridges in the Vale of Purbeck, it straggles out for nearly a kilometre and a half (one mile). Although the village stores has closed, the Post Office survives in one of the two garages together with a small supermarket (only just opened). Few settlements of this size can boast two garages, the second one, at the eastern end of the settlement has a surrogate village stores attached to it. With the re-opening of the Swanage Railway, Harman's Cross acquired a railway station, complete with signal box, and this serves all of the many visitor camping and caravan sites around the village. Another sign of twenty-first century times is Harman's Cross vineyard, no doubt enjoying the benefits of well-drained sandy soils and southerly aspect.

If the western vale is deeply rural, its villages fit remarkably well into this charming scene. Church Knowle belies its original Domesday name *Cnolle*, 'hill-top', since it is much dominated by Knowle Hill of the Chalk ridge to the north. There does seem to

Church Knowle village from Knowle Hill.

be a record of a priest here at the time of the Domesday Book, and the present church, sitting on its knoll just below the Greensand Bench, is the outstanding feature of the village. St Peter's is thirteenth century, with chancel and east window surviving from that time. The present nave was the result of nineteenth century alterations and the north aisle was added at that time. The tower was first built in the fourteenth century, but was largely rebuilt in 1741.

Church Farm, said by some to be the prettiest building in Church Knowle, lies on the opposite side of the road, together with the Old Rectory, rebuilt in the nineteenth century by the Rev. Owen Mansel, who also provided the original Reading Room next to the church. The remainder of the village, mostly Purbeck Stone, but occasionally brick, stretches away westwards to include the other main focus of the village, The New Inn. Like the Greyhound in Corfe Castle, it is really two buildings: the old seventeenth-century thatched cottage has expanded to include the original dairy next door. Situated at the centre of a parish that takes in heathland, the Purbeck Hills, part of the Corfe valley, and the limestone heights of Smedmore, Church Knowle is quintessential Purbeck, knitting together the different Purbeck landscapes in one delightful village. In many ways Church Knowle is the only true remaining village of the western vale of Purbeck. Steeple, although centre of a large parish, now only has its church and Manor House, together with a few other buildings. Tyneham, once the vibrant centre of the far western vale is now deserted and silent, and is likely to remain so in the immediate future. All three are still linked together as being within the benefice of St Edward's at Corfe Castle and the church still brings some unity to life in the western vale.

Langton Matravers, the main street.

The three villages of the limestone lands of southern Purbeck show considerable variety in their landscapes. Although all of the villages are built almost exclusively of local Purbeck Stone, it is their sites and street character that give them their individuality. Langton – the 'long farm or estate' has a main street that extends from the outskirts of Swanage at Coombe to the terraced developments that are almost at the level of the unsheltered open lands of the plateau. Much of the recent growth has been in the small cul-de-sacs that branch off to the north and south of the main street. Small patches of open farmland still survive along the road that steadily climbs westwards through the village. Worth is altogether more compact, focussing on the duck pond and small village green, but with some more modern developments on the southen and eastern sides of the village. Kingston is the village that has probably changed the least over the last few decades, with relatively little new building in the settlement that looks down on Corfe Castle, in whose parish it lies, from the top of its hill.

Although Langton straggles for over a kilometre and a half (one mile), there are three main cores of development in the village. Just beyond Coombe on the main road into Swanage, there is a group of houses that centres on Coombe Farm on the slope of the hill that leads up to the Ship Inn. Coombe Farm is recorded in the Domesday survey, and on the opposite side of Coombe Hill are the gates leading to Leeson House, where a farm probably existed in Saxon times, although the present house, now a Field Study Centre, dates from the early years of the nineteenth century, when it was built by the Reverend John Dampier. More recent housing developments branch off the main street, and include the council houses of Three Acre Lane, award winners in 1952, and the modern housing estates of Serrell's Mead and Steppes Hill, on the other side of the road. At the top of Coombe Hill is the 1884 Ship Inn, and opposite is the eighteenth-century Langton Matravers Farmhouse,with its adjoining eighteenth-century barn. Completing the housing stock in this part of the village are the three rows of Council cottages, known as The Steppes, unusually built of Swanage brick.

St George's church, Langton Matravers.

Beyond the Ship Inn, with its adjacent cottage that housed the original inn, Steps Hill leads down into the valley of the little stream known as the Puck Lake, 'a mischievious stream' that still has a tendency to flood from time to time. Putlake Farm, now an 'adventure farm', lies on the valley side. The 1761 turnpike section of Langton's main street begins just beyond Crack Lane, which was originally Creek Lane, since it gave access to the main stream of Langton parish in the valley to the north. West of Crack Lane is the present commercial heart of the village, lined with neat stone cottages, together with the Post Office and King's Arms public house, first licensed in 1741. In the past other shops offered their services here, including a butcher's and more recently the village bakery, where at an earlier stage there existed a shop that sold groceries and millinery. Here too was Langton's garage, long since disappeared. The parish church of St George occupies a central position in this part of the village. It has mediaeval origins, but it was extensively rebuilt twice in the nineteenth century except for the fifteenth century tower. Rebuilding has resulted in the unusual situation of the roof of the nave being higher than the tower to the west. The old National Schoolroom is on the other side of the main street, although it now serves as the Village Hall.

Two schools are found higher up the hill, St George's First School, and the Old Malthouse, a flourishing preparatory school. These two establishments are the only two remaining out of the nine schools that existed at one time in Langton. Opposite the Old Malthouse is Garfield, a forbidding angular building, originally built for a Langton shopkeeper, but later turned into a school, Garfield School in 1929. Now it has been converted into apartments. Eighteenth and nineteenth century cottages in Arundel Terrace appear

Long House, Langton Matravers (the last house in Langton).

on the southern side of the main street, and Langton really comes to an end with the Council houses of Capstan Field, still faithfully built in local stone, a reminder of the many small quarry workings in this area with their central winches or capstans that were used for bringing the stone to the surface. Opposite was the Top Shop, until recently the oldest surviving shop in the village selling a lively range of goods until it finally succumbed in the 1990s. If Langton began on a farming note at Coombe, it ends in similar fashion, for the last house in the village is a former longhouse , shared between the farmer and his family in one section and their livestock in the other.

Worth has a village landscape entirely different from the long cottage-lined turnpike of Langton.'Worth' refers to an enclosure of farmland, and suggests a Saxon origin. In the centre of the village neat stone cottages cluster tightly around the village pond. Facing the pond on the northern side is Gulliver's Cottage and adjacent to it was the village stores and Post Office, now sadly closed in 2005, although the teashop still remains, serving the countless walkers who spend their weekends rambling over the footpaths leading out to the sea. The attractive village church of St Nicholas lies at the

St Nicholas's church, Worth Matravers.

Worth Matravers village.

top of the slight rise that runs up from the village pond and teashop. It is unusual in that it is almost entirely mediaeval, dating from the very early twelfth century, probably the same age as the nave of St Nicholas at Studland. Under the eaves is a corbel table, characteristic of Norman churches, with carved animal and human heads. The south porch was built in 1774, and the pyramidal section of the tower, a distinguishing feature, like that at Church Knowle, was only added in 1870. It was from this church that the priest commuted along the Priest's Way, to the chapel in the fishing village of Swanage, a journey that ceased in the early sixteenth century.

Worth Matravers,
The Square and Compass.

Beyond to the west is the imposing building of the Old Rectory, for Worth no longer has a resident priest. On the opposite side of the road junction is the old village school, built in 1850 and finally closing in 1922. The schoolroom is today used as the Village Hall. Nearby is Calico Cottage, once the site of a former shop. London Row, a line of nineteenth century quarrymen's cottages, is a reminder of Worth's somewhat tenuous connection with the metropolis. The public house of the Square and Compass, very much a quarrymen's inn, is perhaps another focal point of the village. Like the Greyhound in Corfe Castle it was originally two cottages, and it probably opened as a pub in the early 1700s. Today it has a flourishing trade, not only with the local quarry workers and residents, but also the weekend and summer tourists who can enjoy its obvious links with the busy and adventurous past of this corner of the stone lands of Purbeck

So Worth bids well to be Purbeck's perfect nucleated village. An ancient core of stone cottages has now seen almost inevitable new additions of modern estate developments at the eastern and southern ends of the village. Few visitors to the village ever see the new stone villas, which command views down the valley to Winspit and the lynchets of East Man and West Man. Mists often roll in from the sea, cloaking the village in a grey and clammy shroud, when it has a mysterious atmosphere, quite different from the bright sunny days of summer when tourists gather around the village pond and the bar of the Square and Compass overflows on to its carved and sculptured surrounds.

St James's church, Kingston.

Kingston is the third of the villages of Purbeck's limestone plateau. Curiously, it lies within the parish of Corfe Castle, although it has no obvious links with the much larger village. Although the ownership of Encombe House has changed, it still has the feeling of an estate village – it is still owned by the Scott family. Kingston's older church lies on the eastern side of the village in a position with magnificent views down to Corfe Castle over the Vale of Purbeck. Although it had mediaeval origins, it was completely rebuilt in

The village pump, Kingston.

1833 by the first Earl of Eldon. Although largely replaced by the much larger St James in 1880, it was still used for services until 1921, after which it served as a Village Hall for a short period: in 1979–81 it was converted into use as a private dwelling.

The new St James was built between 1874 and 1880 and is perched high on a mound overlooking the centre of the village. It is one of the great landmarks of southern Purbeck presiding a little gloomily over the village and all of the western part of the vale to the south of Corfe Castle. It was built for the third Earl of Eldon: it is an almost overwhelming structure, quite disproportionate to the small village that it now serves. All of the varieties of stone required for its construction were quarried locally, including the Purbeck Marble for the many shafts and pillars in the interior. The centre of the village, where South Street and West Street meet is known as the Square, surrounded by Purbeck Stone cottages and shaded by the large trees in the churchyard. The village pump, provided by Morton Pitt, Lord of the Manor until 1807 survives, although its handles have been removed. Behind the pump is the cottage that housed the Post Office and Stores before it closed in the 1990s.

The Scott Arms, Kingston and the old Reading Room.

Kimmeridge village.

Perhaps the best known building in the village is the Scott Arms. This public house, with a delightful cover of Virginia creeper, was originally the New Inn, but was then renamed the Eldon Arms. After the earls of Eldon no longer lived at Encombe House it was renamed for a second time, to become the present day Scott Arms. Beyond the Scott Arms, on the other side of the road leading down through hairpin bends to Corfe Castle are other buildings of note. The Bailiff's House and Old Reading Room look across the road to the buildings of St James' School and the Old Schoolhouse, empty since the school closed in 1961. Kingston's late-eighteenth-century Rope and Sailcloth Manufactory has not survived: only the footpath carrying the name Rope Walk marks the point where the boy employees operated the hemp spindles.

Apart from Arne, hiding away at the end of the long road from Ridge and Stoborough, and Tyneham, now deserted and silent, Kimmeridge is one of Purbeck's more remote villages. It can only be seen from the escarpment of limestone that winds around from Swyre Head to Tyneham Cap. Most visitors will see it for the first time as it comes into view when the corner is turned at the top of the hill leading down into the village. It fits perfectly into the lovely enclosed lowland that lies beneath Smedmore Hill. Its one street, mostly lined by pre- nineteenth century thatched cottages, begins by the church of St Nicholas and the tree-shaded Old Parsonage, and loses itself in the shadow of the little rounded hill of Metherills: its continuation meanders down to the sea at the Bay. The church was originally Norman, but was extensively rebuilt in 1872 owing to the excessive weight of the roof on the walls. Two attractive buildings flank the little

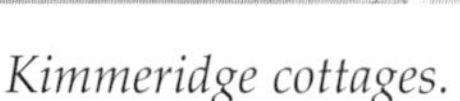

Kimmeridge cottages.

St Nicholas's church, Kimmeridge.

church on either side. To the west is Kimmeridge Farmhouse, enlarged and remodelled in the nineteenth century, although previous farmhouses will have stood here for many centuries. Over the front door is the crest and coat-of-arms of the Mansel family, who feature so importantly in the history of Kimmeridge and its surrounding lands. Mrs John Mansel inherited it from her uncle the Reverend John Clavell in 1833. On the opposite side is the Old Parsonage built by Mrs Mansel's widowed sister so that Kimmeridge could have its own parson.

Purbeck's village landscape, though still traditional in many ways, is changing. Although many of the villages still retain cottages that date back to the eighteenth century or before, new buildings, usually still built in local Purbeck Stone, are beginning to appear; they even dominate in settlements such as Harman's Cross and Stoborough. It is perhaps the demise of the village store that is to be most regretted, for an essential focus of village life has been lost. Few agricultural workers live in the villages now, and most residences are retirement or commuter homes: some professionals even work from their homes, enjoying the benefits of computers, fax machines and the internet. Changes of this kind are inevitable, but Purbeck's villages are still a lively and essential element in the rural landscape.

Chapter Nine

Purbeck's Townscapes

Ewart Johns, in his *British Townscapes*, wrote 'Throughout history, and archaeology can assure us, throughout prehistory also, man has designed his villages, his towns and his cities not only for protection, comfort and economy, but also ,in some measure, for the satisfaction of his sense of the propriety of the shapes in which he and his family should live'. He suggests therefore that there are two complementary ways of looking at our townscapes: the buildings that make up the urban scene should have a purposeful function, and they should also be pleasing aesthetically. He also suggests that they may be described simply as they are viewed by the casual observer of townscape, or that the more critical student of the urban scene may wish to make judgemental comment on buildings and their arrangement within the town. Purbeck's two towns, Wareham and Swanage, offer ample opportunity for intelligent description and critical appraisal.

Wareham, the Frome.

It might be argued that Wareham, located on its site between the Frome to the south and the Piddle to the north, is not really in Purbeck at all, since it lies to the north of the bounding river Frome. Although it may have had a separate existence as a Saxon walled fortress town, and as a mediaeval river port, the town has become increasingly part of the life of the peninsula that lies to the south over the River Frome. Today it is the essential gateway town to Purbeck: all road traffic passes through the town or along its western by-pass, rail travellers to Purbeck still alight at Wareham station, although in the future they may well find that they can complete their jouney into the heartland of Purbeck by rail. Purbeck is administered from Wareham, with the District Council having its headquarters in Westport House, overlooking the Frome: many Purbeck people shop in Wareham for essentials and the majority of Purbeck's teenagers finish their full-time education in well-esteemed Purbeck School on the outskirts of the town. To a degree, Wareham is cut off to the north by the dark conifers of Wareham Forest and the heathy no-man's land of Holton Heath, with only the ever-busy main road linking it northwards to the urban mass of Poole and Bournemouth. It has the feel of a town that has a southward looking prospect embracing the lands of Purbeck from the Great Heath southwards. Standing on the

Swanage, the beach.

attractive quayside by the River Frome, the aspect southwards is of the special Purbeck landscape with which Wareham can identify.

Swanage, once fishing village and stone-shipping port, and later Victorian seaside resort, is very much a part of the essential Purbeck scene. Until the new estates began to grow, Swanage was a stone town, at one with the underlying Jurassic geology. Unlike red-brick Wareham, Swanage is a grey town, with its stone villas and terraces rising away from the sea front: it sits not on a cramped site between two rivers, but has expanded southwards over the limestone plateau, and northwards along the red cliffs of its bay, and more slowly westwards into the pastures and copses of the Vale of Purbeck. Today it is described as one of the gateway towns to the Jurassic Coast, but it is still Purbeck's seaside, and service and entertainment centre for many Purbeck residents. It has a vibrant commercial centre, still set in Victorian surroundings and sustains a busy social scene. In winter it is retirement Purbeck, emphasised by the increasing conversion of hotels to retirement apartments: in summer, holiday Purbeck adds its youthful face and pace to the Swanage scene.

West Walls, Wareham.

The townscape of Wareham owes much to its site between the two rivers. Although there is evidence of occupation of the Wareham area before Saxon times, the present form of Wareham owes its clear rectangular pattern to the earthworks that were built in the time of Alfred. As Treves wrote 'It is unique in this: that it is a fortified town, that lies within the encompass of its own entrenchments and that the great ramparts which still shut it in, cannot be less than one thousand years old.' Asser, Alfred's biographer, described the site of Wareham as 'a most secure situation, except on the western side where it is joined to the mainland.' In Alfred's time Wareham, one of his fortified *burhs* was the fourth largest town in Wessex: only Winchester, Wallingford (which has a similar town layout to Wareham) and Southwark were larger. The earthworks that were built to protect the Saxon town still survive today.

On the north they overlook the floodplain of the Piddle, and the walk along North Walls provides handsome views across the low-lying water meadows to the north and the conifers on the gravel plateaux beyond. West Walls, where the need for defence was greatest, extend the earthworks overlooking the Piddle down to the banks of the Frome. On this western side the defence function was re-activated in the Second World War when the walls were strengthened and pressed into service as an anti-tank barricade. On the north-west corner of West Walls there is an open space known as the Cockpits where cockfighting once took place. On the highest part of the earthworks of West Walls is Bloody Banks, a site of some notoriety. A hermit, Peter de Pomfret, was

Wareham from the south.

said to have been hanged here in the time of King John: later during the time of the Bloody Assizes of Judge Jeffreys, ringleaders of the Monmouth Rebellion were tried in Dorchester and then five men were hung, drawn and quartered on this site on the West Walls. To the south of the point where the main road crosses West Walls the outer ditch of the walls reaches its best development.

Just within West Walls at the southern end of the earthworks was the site of Wareham Castle. It was probably built in Norman times, and it continued to function as a state prison and had its own military garrison. As Corfe Castle to the south grew in importance owing to it superior defensive position, Wareham Castle began its long decline. The date of its destruction is not known, but the site changed hands many times until it was bought by local solicitor Seymer Clark in the mid-nineteenth century. He built the imposing villa known as Castle Close which still stands on the castle mound today. The prominent house can be clearly seen across the water meadows of the Frome on the approach along the causeway from Stoborough. It forms part of the delightful prospect of the town from the south, where the gravel terrace rises steeply from the river, and the houses of Wareham appear half hidden by trees that climb up from the river's banks.

East Walls extend southwards from the north-east corner of North Walls. Where the two meet is an open space known as the Bowling Green. Historical records indicate that it was indeed used as a bowling green. Fairs were also held there in the past, particularly the town fairs of 1858 and 1864. The East Walls form another pleasant walking area, which Treves thought 'makes an excellent promenade, much affected by children at all times and by young men and women on high days and holidays.' Views eastwards over the sports grounds and allotments eventually lead to the water meadows along the lower reaches of the Frome. The river formed the fourth element in the defences of Wareham. The town's original name appeared as *Werham* in the Anglo Saxon Chronicle of 786: this simply meant 'the homestead by the weir'. The weir on the Frome was simply a fish trap across the river used to catch both salmon and eels.

Before the Frome began to silt up Wareham was a busy river port. In William of Malmesbury's chronicle, it is stated that 'Wareham was already a recognised cross-channel port in the early eighth century'. As time progressed the attention of seamen and merchants was turned downstream, and an attempt was made to develop a quay at Hamworthy on Poole Harbour. Poole first recorded shipping movements in 1170, and it received its charter as a port in 1248: the demise of Wareham as a port had begun. Ships could anchor safely at Poole and did not have to wait for the tide to carry them up the silting estuary to Wareham Quay. The port still survived and even in 1347 Wareham supplied three ships and 59 men for Edward III's campaign to Calais. In the same year, the Wareham ship *Margarete* was arrested by the keepers of the port of Poole and there seems little trace of trading activity from Wareham's port after this date. By 1745, decay was all too evident and money had to be raised locally to maintain a decent waterfront at Wareham.

Wareham, South Bridge.

Treves paints a charming picture of the Quay in the early twentieth century: 'By the bridge is the quay – a wide capacious square – which was crowded and bustling when Wareham did trade with the world. It is now deserted, except for two boys who are fishing and a pedlar who has fallen asleep in the sun from the fatigue of watching them'. Today the 'capacious square' is a busy car park, and new buildings have replaced all of those destroyed in the great fire of 1762. On the eastern side, the granary run by the Oakley Brothers in the latter half of the nineteenth century now houses a restaurant, and along the northern side The Quay Inn and another restaurant look out across the square to the Stoborough water meadows and the distant Creech Barrow and the Purbeck Hills. In summer pleasure craft make the long journey up the reed-fringed estuary from Poole and visitors can enjoy themselves in Wareham's teashops and hotels.

The Quay today is the highest point of navigation on the Frome for most vessels: beyond is South Bridge. The earliest bridge which carried traffic southwards into Purbeck was built of stone and had seven arches. When John Leland visited the town

Wareham, the Corn Exchange.

in about 1540, he recorded a bridge with six arches. Two hundred years later it was replaced by another structure, with five arches. With increasing traffic in the twentieth century, this bridge could no longer cope with the steady stream of vehicles entering and leaving Purbeck. It was replaced in 1927 with the present three-arched structure. For a short while there was the somewhat strange sight of both bridges existing side by side.

Within the rectangle of the Walls and the River Frome Wareham is essentially a grid-iron town, a legacy of Saxon town planning. The street plan is based on the cruciform pattern of the four main streets, which meet in the centre of the town, and run out to gaps in the defensive ramparts: Northport and Westport are names that survive to indicate the position of the breaks in the defences. In the spaces left between the main streets and the ramparts the grid-iron pattern is completed by self-styled 'lanes', which have seen infill housing develop over the centuries. The names of the 'lanes' derive from people that may have lived there, vanished features or occupational associations. In Treves' time he found 'the little place shrunken that it occupies but a part of the area enclosed by the entrenchments... Those who know the town say that the lanes between the gardens are old streets and that there were once houses along Mill Lane, Bell Lane and Howard's Lane.' Infilling has changed what Treves saw: the odd thatched cottage survives, but most of the brick houses are of a later date.

Although the street plan gives a basic outline to today's townscape, many of the buildings along the streets converging on the Square in the centre of the town are of eighteenth and nineteenth century age. During the Great Fire of 1762 much of the housing around the Square was destroyed: two thirds of the town was destroyed and 133 houses were lost during the blaze. Thus rebuilding brought a later style 'unpretentious and homely in appearance', to many of the new buildings, with thatch being banned in the town centre.

Today, the Square, with its controlling traffic lights, has a broad and airy appearance about it . Before the fire, the southern end of North Street was the site of a particularly dense group of buildings, known as 'The Shambles' or Middle Row, where a number of shopkeepers operated. After the fire these were not allowed to be rebuilt, and posterity has benefitted, particularly in the age of motor vehicles. The two most prominent buildings around the Square are the Red Lion Hotel, and opposite it, the Town Hall. The Red Lion replaced a previous coaching inn, and in the nineteenth century it had the reputation of Wareham's premier hotel. The present Town Hall designed by G.R Crickmay, the Weymouth architect, replaced the old building that was

Wareham, the Red Lion.

Wareham, the thatched King's Arms.

rebuilt after the fire. It now houses the Council Chamber, and the Corn Exchange on the ground floor is now used for social events. Crickmay's creation is not to everybody's liking. John Newman, in his *Buildings of England* refers to it as 'a wretchedly mean affair, all the meaner for being at the central crossroads of the town.' Northwards, most of the buildings are late eighteenth or nineteenth century of brick and tile construction, although new shop fronts have often modified more elegant older frontages. The 'Anglebury' is one of Wareham's oldest buildings, dating back to the sixteenth century, although the front of this hotel-cum-restaurant is eighteenth century. Farther along North Street is the King's Arms, which escaped the fire and still possesses a thatched roof.

Wareham, St John's Hill.

South Street is a continuation of the shopping area of North Street, but also has several other interesting buildings. The Manor House, Wareham's only Grade I listed building, on the eastern side of South Street, is set slightly back from the main street, but nevertheless has an imposing front. It was built for George Gould in 1712, and is notable for its fourteen windows symmetrically placed on the front elevation, with a similar number on the back. Part of its spacious garden was sold off for the development of a shopping centre. On the opposite side of South Street, again set back from the main street frontage is the old Unitarian Chapel, a Palladian-style building built in 1830: it now houses the local Conservative Club. Farther down South Street, nearer the

The Black Bear, Wareham.

River Frome is the elegant Black Bear Hotel, with its magnificent bow windows. It was first mentioned in 1722, but was destroyed in the Great Fire, and rebuilt in its present form. The fine effigy of the black bear has obvious connections with the sport of bear-baiting. Just off South Street is the little shopping area of St John's Hill. It was the site of a former church, although its early names appear to have been Sawpits Green or Sawpitgreen. Mint House on the southern side may be the site of a Saxon mint, indicating the importance of Wareham in the time of Athelstan. Today St John's Hill is a charming little urban cameo, with a pleasing mix of shops and residences.

East Street leads from the Square to Bestwalls (a corruptive form of by-the-east wall). Unlike the other three streets that make up the cruciform street pattern, East Street is not part of the contemporary commercial centre. Originally it had two public houses, The Three Tuns, next door to the Town Hall, and The Duke of Wellington. The former closed in 1906, but The Duke of Wellington has survived into the twenty-first century. Opposite are the Almshouses, which were originally founded in 1418, although the present building, that survived the fire, dates from 1741. They have now been converted into private dwellings. Farther east there are examples of nineteenth century villas that were built for the more affluent. Few of the old cottages that once lined East Street now survive. West Street is different. It does not have the cul-de-sac atmosphere of East Street: it leads westwards to the villas and schools of Worgret Road and the main road westwards to Wool and Dorchester. Near the Square it has its own extension of the central shopping area, with the Rex Cinema, still universally popular, its most unexpected building.

Wareham, East Street.

Although Wareham possessed as many as twelve churches in the Middle Ages, four that survive to the present day can be said to make some genuine contribution to the townscape. St Martin's located on a bluff that overlooks the floodplain of the River Piddle is said to be the most complete Saxon church in Dorset. St Mary's, on a similar bluff overlooking the Frome, was much rebuilt in the mid-nineteenth century and might well have been the most complete Saxon church in the country were it not for this restoration of its nave and aisles. Holy Trinity, although disused since the 1762 fire still stands and is best remembered as a memorial to John Hutchins, its last rector and author of the remarkable *History and Antiquities of the County of Dorset*. The United Reform church in Church Street belongs to another, more modern era. Built in 1689 it was largely destroyed in the Great Fire but was rebuilt in the same year.

St Martin's is almost unnoticed by those who drive into Wareham from Northport and pass through the steep cutting that leads up to North Street. The Saxon church dates from 1030. The nave survives from the eleventh century, although the north aisle was added in the twelfth century. Wall paintings are a prominent feature of the interior, the earliest probably being twelfth century. It was only used for marriages and christenings from about 1736, although it was used as a shelter for the homeless after the Great Fire of 1762. However, it was finally restored in 1935. Its outstanding monument is the effigy of Lawrence of Arabia, in full Arab dress, which can be seen in the north aisle.

If St Martin's is perhaps unnoticed, then St Mary's is one of Wareham's most cherished landmarks. Slightly aloof on its low bluff, it dominates the Quay, and its tower can be seen from across the watermeadows from either Stoborough or the by-pass. Its floodlit image casts a ghostly aura over the riverside scene, and on sunny days its reflection in the Frome is picture postcard Dorset at its best. The restored nave is unremarkable, but is redeemed somewhat by the tiny chapel of St Edward, where the body of the murdered Edward the Martyr was kept before its removal to Shaftesbury. This chapel is part of the original Saxon Church and is slightly below the level of the main church.

Holy Trinity, Wareham.

Holy Trinity may well have been a chapel dedicated to St Andrew before Norman times but appears in documents as Holy Trinity in 1163. After it fell into disuse it was first used as a school in 1830, but it eventually closed. Latterly it has been used as an art gallery and is now the Purbeck Information and Heritage Centre. Its squat tower dominates the riverside scene on the western side of South Bridge, and neatly complements its sister church to the east. The Congregational (or United Reform) church is one of the more important buildings in the lanes of Wareham. Its distinctive style adds interest to the other buildings of Church Street. It was much enlarged in the nineteenth century and still plays an important part in the religious life of Wareham.

United Reform church, Wareham.

Although the Priory, close to St Mary's, is now an elegant hotel, with beautiful riverside gardens, it does have an important religious history. The original building on the site of the present day hotel, was founded by Aldhelm, the Bishop of Sherborne. It was recorded as 'a convent of nuns' in 876. Later it suffered from Viking raids from which it never fully recovered, although it housed a small community of monks until the Dissolution. Parts of the present house had their origin in the early sixteenth century, but there is now little evidence of its former religious importance.

Frederick Treves wrote of Swanage in the early twentieth century 'Swanage, as I knew it some thirty-five years ago, was a queer little town with a rambling High Street and a jumble of picturesque cottages of Purbeck Stone, whose rough roofs were much given to gable ends and dormer windows... Now it is the scene of a feverish struggle

The Priory Hotel and Lady St Mary's, Wareham.

between rival builders, who fight to cover the land with copious red brick in as little time as possible.' Treves wrote this in 1906, and the Ordnance Map of Swanage at that time shows the 'rambling High Street': roads were already beginning to climb the limestone land to the south, and the first villas had appeared north of the railway station. He also noted that 'The curve of the sandy bay is swept by a long brick coal shed, and is palisaded by the unlovely backs of unashamed homes'. One hundred years later he would find it difficult to recognise the Swanage of the twenty-first century. The High Street hardly rambles but it is now a part of the one way system without which Swanage could not function. Some picturesque cottages still remain in places like Church Hill and around the Mill Pond, but many more have been demolished. Seaside Swanage now lines the cliff top as far as distant Shep's Hollow, although an unstable cliff will continue to threaten. New housing estates have spread well beyond Victoria Avenue and New Swanage reaches towards Ulwell and Whitecliff. Villas and terraces have swept up from the High Street to the south and housing estates cling to the slopes that lead to Townsend and its former quarries, and Belle Vue Farm to the west.

Parts of the townscape of central Swanage are perhaps unremarkable. A short walk from the 1885 railway station, now busy again since the reopening of the line to Norden in 1995, along Station Road and Institute Road to the Square at the seaward end of the High Street reveals terraces of shops that serve local people and the summer visitors. This crowded and congested shopping core is very different to the open and more attractive shopping area of North and South Street Wareham. Some say that

Station Road should never have become the main shopping street – it could have been an area of landscaped gardens with the Swanage Brook as a centrepiece resembling the Lower Pleasure Gardens in Bournemouth. At the seaward end of Station Road, on the opposite side of the road is the Mowlem Theatre, a sixties building that is not to everyone's architectural taste. Functionally it provides Swanage with a theatre, a cinema, and attractive community rooms and restaurant. It replaces the Mowlem Institute, a solid and more attractive building that was constructed by John Mowlem, one of the great benefactors of Swanage 'for the benefit and the mutual improvement of the working classes'. In order for the terraces on the seaward side of Institute Road to be built much of the land occupied by the bankers, where stone was banked up ready for export in the days before it was sent out by rail, had to be reclaimed. This area had been used for storing and working stone for nearly 200 years. Rails still embedded in the promenade are all that remains of a project to link Langton's stone quarries with the new pier. Institute Road, with its shops facing one another across one of the narrowest parts of Swanage's one way system, opens out into the Square, on which stands Swanage's relatively new Heritage Centre.

Swanage Railway, the approach to the station.

The road curving away out of the Square towards the Pier has one notable building, the Royal Victoria Hotel. It was originally built by Thomas Chapman in 1664 as the Manor House but was later transformed into the Manor House Hotel by William Morton Pitt who added two wings and a stable block. It achieved its 'Royal' acknowledgement after the Princess Victoria and her mother spent a night there in 1833. The Prince of Wales spent a night there in 1856 whilst on a walking tour of Dorset. It survived as a hotel until the 1970s, but for nearly thirty years it has provided apartment accommodation, with fine views over Swanage Bay.

Swanage, the old tramway on the Promenade.

Swanage Pier.

Swanage's first pier was built in 1859-60 by James Walton a contractor from London. Although it was open to traffic in 1862, the scheme for linking it to the Langton quarries was never completed, largely the result of lack of co-operation of the owners of land intervening between the pier and the quarries. By all accounts it was a somewhat rough and ready construction, certainly not a place to stroll and take in the sea air. People complained about its inconveniences, the danger of tripping between the planks, the lack of seating and the absence of a handrail. The new pier, much more in keeping with Swanage's growing reputation as a seaside resort was built in 1895-6 and opened in 1897. It allowed day trippers to make the sea journey from growing Bournemouth to Swanage: 10,000 visitors trod the planks of the new pier on Bank Holiday Monday in the first year. Those holidaying in Swanage could take the steamers to Lulworth, or farther afield to Weymouth, the Isle of Wight or even across the Channel to Cherbourg. The old pier continued to be used by coaling vessels until the 1920s, but the new one is still in use by paddle steamers such as the evergreen *Waverley*, which still plies its way between Swanage and Bournemouth and other resorts each summer.

Swanage, the Clock Tower.

Between the pier and Peveril Point there are three present-day elements in the townscape of Swanage that require some comment. The original Grosvenor Hotel on this stretch of coast began life as The Grove, a 'marine residence' built for the Coventry family in 1838. It became the home of the retired London contractor Thomas Docwra in 1866 and it was further expanded in the late nineteenth and early twentieth century. In the grounds of the Grosvenor the Clock Tower still exists – a legacy of Victorian gothic. It was originally erected at the southern end of London Bridge in 1854 as a memorial to the first Duke of Wellington, but within a few years it was increasingly seen as an obstruction and was demolished in 1866. George Burt had it carefully packed up and brought to Swanage where he presented it to Thomas Docwra who rebuilt it in his grounds: it has no clock face.

The Grosvenor survived as a hotel until the 1980s when it was demolished for redevelopment. A marina, with accompanying waterside homes was proposed for the site, but it never received Parliamentary approval. The first phase of 32 waterside residences was built, decorated in pastel shades that have never really fitted into the landscape of the Peveril Peninsula. Other remaining phases were never built, and the remaining site of the Grosvenor was acquired by Wessex Water for the construction of a new sewage works, built in Purbeck Stone to merge into Swanage's grey urban townscape. So the Peveril Peninsula has a strange mix of buildings – a surviving piece of Victoriana, and two ultra-modern constructions that add an alien note to this seaward projection of Swanage which ends in the reefs off the Point.

Swanage: flats for the Marina development.

Swanage: the Town Hall.

The high Street begins at the Square and drifts away westwards through stone terraces, villas and newer infill housing to end at Herston amongst Swanage suburbia, take-away shops and the always welcome view of the heights of Godlingston Hill to the north. Shops line the first narrow section of the High Street with its modern well- proportioned and elegant Public Library. Lloyds Bank replaced an earlier row of shops in 1896, and The Red Lion and The Anchor Inns survive from an earlier stage. Higher up the High Street, Swanage's Town Hall, was built in the 1880s on the site of the Drong Cottages, typical of the low elevation stone cottages of their time. George Burt brought more of London to Swanage when he decided to bring the front of the Cheapside Mercers' Hall, which was being rebuilt, to be incorporated in the new Town Hall. Although the front had suffered grievously from London's pollution, the sea air of Swanage seems to have had a remarkable cleansing effect. Inside a spacious open staircase leads up to an equally impressive Council Chamber. Today's imposing façade gives the Town Hall a grandiose appearance, and bears witness to George Burt's penchant for bringing London's architecture to Dorset's seaside. The two-faced clock may also have come from a demolished City church. A tiny lock-up survives behind the Town Hall. Originally built near the parish church, it was moved when the church was rebuilt.

Looking up the High Street from the Town Hall is the grey, somewhat foreboding mass of Purbeck House. The original building was relatively small, and was probably early seventeenth century, and was enlarged in the early nineteenth century before George Burt bought it in 1857 and lived there for seventeen years before he decided to rebuild it to the design of local architect Crickmay. Its grandiloquent style has been dubbed 'Scottish Baronial'. One quoted critic thought that this building 'of which the aim was obviously beauty, should have achieved so startling an ugliness'. Once again George Burt brought fragments of London to Swanage: iron columns and stone balustrades came from Billingsgate market, waste stone chippings for wall facings arrived from The Albert Memorial in Hyde Park. Once he had enlarged the grounds of Purbeck House more London memorabilia began to appear in the gardens. George Burt died in 1894, but the Burt family continued to live in Purbeck House until 1920. It then remained empty until it was acquired by the Convent of Mercy, a teaching order of Roman Catholic nuns in 1935. Another change of use came in the 1990s when it became The Purbeck House Hotel. This seemed almost a reversal of current trends when so many of Swanage's hotels were being replaced by flats in situ, or demolished and completely rebuilt as apartment blocks. It remains as a fitting memorial to the Burt family and to George in particular.

Swanage: Purbeck House.

Slightly to the west in High Street is the church built by the Wesleyan Methodists in 1886, 'the best Victorian Gothic in town'. Nicholas Pevsner commented 'the Gothic front with an overstressed octagonal steeple and flowering tracery is spectacular, the side anti-climatically utilitarian'. Its steeple is one of the landmarks of the inner townscape of Swanage, and one wry comment suggests that its dominance of the tower of the parish church was deliberate. George Burt gave a large sum of money towards the spire and laid one of the foundation stones. The large Memorial Hall on the east side was built in 1907.

To venture beyond the Methodist church to the west is to enter a Swanage that is lacking in architectural interest and urban character. However, to turn down Church Hill, past the cross and its circle of steps, is to experience one of Swanage's most delightful urban charms – the Mill Pond and the cosy stone cottages that still surround it. Although these cottages were threatened with demolition in the 1930s, they still survive today, although they have been much repaired and improved. The mill house bears the inscription 'Ben Barlow, Mill Wright of Southampton fecit 1754'. There is evidence of a mill here several centuries before, and corn milling did continue until 1928.

Swanage: the Mill Pond.

Church Hill winds around the parish church of St Mary, passes the Tithe Barn on the east and joins King's Road by crossing the crowfoot-brightened stretch of the little brook. Culverted for much of its course through Swanage, it emerges here to give an almost sylvan setting for the parish church with its tree-lined course.

Swanage: St Mary's.

Although Swanage was originally such a small fishing village that a priest or curate had to travel from Worth Matravers to take services there, it grew sufficiently in mediaeval times for it to become a separate parish in 1506. A substantial church did exist in Swanage from this time onwards, but only the tower remains after significant rebuilding of the church in 1859–60 and 1907–8. The tower may be of early thirteenth century origin, although the lower sections are probably fourteenth century and the upper ones seventeenth century: it may have been a refuge or a fortified structure. The rebuilt church gives an airy and spacious interior impression. The first rebuilding involved the present nave and south transept, whilst the later additions in 1907–8 virtually created a new church parallel to and west of the original structure.

If Wareham's ancient protection was its ramparts, Swanage's present defences are the Shore Road seawall and the promenade that runs along Shore Road. The seawall gives much needed protection against the easterly wind-driven waves, not to say gales that lash the coast from time to time. Groynes give added protection by keeping the beach in place. However, with the construction of the 1993 jetty to carry away flood water from Swanage, changes, already noted elsewhere, had become apparent in the beach. Accumulation of sand to the south of the new jetty meant that the northern section of the beach was becoming starved of sand. Questions of how long such losses of beach material can continue were constantly being asked. However, new groynes were put in place and an extensive beach replenishment was carried out in 2005-2006. Swanage's beach is one of its greatest assets: its continued existence is essential to the future of the resort.

Swanage: St Mary's – the tower.

So Purbeck's two townscapes are completely different. Wareham, initially hemmed in by its ramparts and its River Frome, focusses on the crossroads of the Square in the middle of the town. Its gridiron plan readily relates to the old entrances to the town through the ramparts, and today yields much of interest to the inquisitive observer. Rebuilding after the Great Fire has created a townscape of red brick and tile, that contrasts strongly with those areas unaffected by the conflagration, where thatch does occasionally survive.

Swanage is only really constrained by the sea. From the little fishing village and later stone port, no ramparts have controlled its growth. Treves was concerned by its spreading growth and this expansion has continued to the south, the north and the west. No fire has enforced change, only timely and needed demolition of unsafe or unhealthy buildings has changed the inner townscape. Herston straggles away to the west: New Swanage, with its strange mixture of styles, has pushed towards Ballard Down.

Chapter Ten

Retrospect and Prospect

This book began with an overview of Purbeck from one of its highest summits, Creech Barrow; it ends with a retrospective journey from the sea-lashed land of Peveril's rocky peninsula, through the heartland of Purbeck and leaving through its gateway town of Wareham. Such a traverse passes through most of Purbeck's landscapes, with an opportunity for a final glimpse at each of them from a suitable vantage point.

Standing high on the Downs, a grassy expanse that rises westwards from Peveril Point, a view is revealed that embraces most of Swanage, its coastline and the backdrop of the

The Downs, Swanage.

eastern Purbeck Hills. On a day in high summer, white sails drift across the blue of Swanage Bay, and the crowded beach on the edge of the bay shimmers in the heat haze.The distant hills form a series of billowing curves that run away westwards from Ballard Down across the Ulwell Gap to high Godlingston and the faintest hint of the barrows of Ailwood Down. Swanage spreads away into the vale to the west where Windmill Knap and the other sandstone hillocks fade away towards Knitson and the other farms in the shadow of the hills. From the airy spread of the Downs the route through Swanage is followed along the western edge of the terraces and villas that spread up from the heart of the town. It passes the thriving Cottage Hospital, built by the family of George Burt as a memorial to their father, and first opened in 1895.The road slips past Mountscar First School, first opened by John Ernest Mowlem in 1897, curves round rows of typical Swanage terraces and joins the familiar High Street almost opposite Church Hill.

Steam at Corfe.

High Street leads westwards to the junction with the main road into Swanage where new views of the Purbeck hills open up to the north. Individual houses and terraces line the southern side of the road before Herston's estates appear with the fine Middle School half-hidden by conifers on the opposite side. Instead of taking the Valley Road through the centre of the Vale of Purbeck, the old turnpike through Langton Matravers is followed after the turning at Coombe. Langton renews memories of village Purbeck with its long main street full of historical interest and some of Purbeck's finest stone cottages. From the top of Langton's almost mile-long street another of Purbeck's landscapes is encountered again – the Landscape of Stone.

Acton, the nucleated quarrymen's village nestles to the south, and the road to Kingston flows easily over the plateau of stone-walled fields After Gallows Gore, curiously named but likely to refer to a triangular plot of land at the site, quarries in the Purbeck Beds appear on the northern side of the road, and views begin to open up across the vale to the north, and the Purbeck Hills and the heathland beyond. Southwards the limestone plateau stretches away towards the sea, with the valley system that drains down to Chapman's Pool breaking up the table-top flatness of the landscape of stone. After the converted Afflington Barn, a layby on the southern side of the road allows a halt and a view northwards towards the centrepiece of the Purbeck Hills, the gaps at Corfe Castle and their ruined fortress. Corfe village pushes its way south towards the common, much changed and more open since the cutting back of the gorse and bracken. There may be a glimpse of the four-carriage passenger train toiling its way up the Affington bank after it has left Corfe Station. Village Purbeck is encountered again as the road dips down towards Kingston, and there is another chance to appre-

Corfe Castle silhouetted at sunset.

ciate the Cathedral of Purbeck, as St James's in the village is sometimes called. The welcome of the Virginia creeper-clad Scott Arms is for once ignored as the road begins its hairpin descent down the slope of the Purbeck Beds. It passes across the outcrop of the Purbeck Marble, with reminders of old workings at Afflington to the east and Blashenwell to the west. Corfe Common suddenly appears ahead, with the corrugations caused by the hauling of marble from the quarries across to the working yards in Corfe Castle. Descent down into Corfe village takes the route across the bogs that had to be reclaimed before the turnpike could be completed.

Corfe's long East Street rises and falls like a minor switchback, the result of the sandstone ridges that run east-west through the sands and clays of the Wealden Beds. Open cul-de-sacs of twentieth century developments, faithful to Purbeck's stone, push out to east and west before the heart of the village, so rich in legend and history, is reached. Corfe Castle's Square has never coped with the age of the motor car: the view of its elegant buildings suffers from passing and parked vehicles. St Edward's church dominates from its grassy mound, and village bakery, Post Office, National Trust Shop and Sweet Shop complete a scene probably the busiest in village Purbeck.

The nightmare bend in the Wareham Road takes the visitor past the Elizabethan Uvedale's House on the eastern side and the half-hidden East or Boar Mill beyond the millpond on the Byle Brook. Corfe's road to Wareham now passes through the remarkable defile cut by the tiny Byle stream. When thunder breaks over Corfe, with its accompanying downpours, it is sometimes flooded and the only road out of Purbeck, bar diversions to Studland, is closed.

East Mill, Corfe Castle.

The road beyond the gap pushes through enclosing trees before reaching the huge roundabout that gives access to the Wytch Farm oilfield to the north-east. Northwards the road slips between two large pools, once the sites of ball clay workings, usually only visible when the birches and chestnuts have lost their leaves in winter. Norden to the west was the centre of ball clay mining to the north of Corfe, but today only birch-clad spoil heaps and quiet pools remain since the last workings closed at the end of the twentieth century. Through the scatter of cottages beyond the railway bridge, the road passes through pastures reclaimed from the heath before reaching the Halfway House Inn. Now for the first time Purbeck's heath appears on either side of the road. Tramway rails once crossed the road in the little dip to the north of Halfway House – a reminder of the busy traffic in clay from the pits to the south to Ridge Wharf. Today the heathland on either side is fenced off, but a glimpse to the east will reveal the National Nature Reserve of Hartland Moor beyond Soldiers Road. Gorse seems

The Quay, Wareham.

almost perennially in bloom along the banks above the road, contrasting with the purples and mauves of the heather in high summer.

The road leaves the heath at the entrance to Stoborough, and after the traverse through the village, the floodplain of the Frome is reached with its causeway pointing the way to Wareham on its dry terraces to the north. After crossing South Bridge a turn takes the visitor into the busy Quay car park, where Treves' snoozing pedlar had been watching boys fishing. One last prospect of Purbeck now remains. Across the waters of the Frome a line of poplars is a sylvan screen to filter the distant view of Purbeck. Creech Barrow dominates the view, rising conically above the woods and fields of Cotness. The ridge of the Purbeck Hills stretches away to the east and west, hiding the heartland of Purbeck. The Frome's bounding water meadows fill the foreground and Redcliffe's wooded knoll to the east overshadows the masts of the yachts moored in the lower reaches of the river.

After a reluctant pause, the traveller turns into Wareham's South Street, and passes through rebuilt Wareham, now risen from the ashes of the Great Fire. The sturdy Red Lion Hotel, in its elegant red brick, faces across the Square to Crickmay's Town Hall, still not loved by all. Higher up North Street, the thatched King's Arms slumbers away cosily, and just before the descent to the Piddle bridge, St Martin's and Lawrence of Arabia bid a fitting historical farewell to those leaving Purbeck. Once through Northport, Wareham's ancient northern gateway, the Piddle floodplain and half-hidden North Mill slip away. The bridge over the railway takes the visitor to suburban Northmoor Park, the straggle of houses and terraces of Sandford and the rhododendrons and birchy thickets that line the road through Holton Heath.

Retrospect has revived the images of the landscapes of Purbeck at the beginning of the twenty-first century. Prospect seeks to peer into the Purbeck crystal ball of future landscapes. As with all landscapes, those of Purbeck will change. Some of the changes will be inevitably natural, others will be man-induced. Looking forward fifty years is hazardous, but some ideas of how Purbeck's landscapes may change can be briefly discussed.

Physical change will happen along the coast. Poole Harbour will continue to silt up, particularly in Purbeck's many northern creeks, and salt marsh will grow and extend to fill bays like Arne and Brands. Studland's dune coast will continue to suffer. Already strategic retreat is expecting land to be lost at Knoll Beach and Middle Beach. In fifty years time perhaps the old cliff line at Studland will once again be lapped by the waters of the bay. There will be change in the coastal landscape of the Chalk. Will

Erosion, Middle Beach Studland.

Old Harry suffer the same fate as his wife? Will new caves break through the chalk or old ones' roofs collapse? Purbeck's landslide coasts will remain unstable and Punfield Cove and Durlston Bay will see new scars in their cliffs as unstable slopes collapse. Swanage's unstable cliffs north of Shore Road will continue to slip and slide and owners of cliff-top properties will watch changes nervously.

Purbeck's sturdy southern stone coast will perhaps see less change in fifty years for limestone resists the sea well and only minor collapses will occur. Chapman's Pool is different: landslides happen every year and Molly's Garden will change and slip away towards the sea. All of Kimmeridge's shale coast is unstable and gentle retreat will occur, and the Coast Path will need many backward changes over fifty years. Beyond Kimmeridge unstable Brandy Bay will witness new cliff falls. If the undercliff below Gad Cliff has shown little change in recent years, will this inactivity continue? Worbarrow's Wealden cliffs will remain unstable and the great landslides at the northern end will continue, perhaps to bite away more of Flower's Barrow's Iron Age fort. Inland the physical landscape will change little. Purbeck's little streams will

Chapman's Pool.

The Purbeck vineyard, Harman's Cross.

Maize field, Blashenwell.

erode only slowly: temporary change with flood waters should be better controlled in urban Swanage, and Corfe's streams may annoyingly flood from time to time, perhaps more often, if climatic change has its way.

Forecasting change in the human landscape of Purbeck is necessarily more difficult. Heathland landscapes may benefit from the changes that have been begun in the Heathland Projects of the early twenty-first century. Mineral exploitation on the heathland will change. Today's large ball-clay pits will have been landscaped, in the fashion of Squirrel's Cottage; perhaps new ones may have appeared, subject to ever more stringent regulations. Will B.P. have ceased its operation in the heathlands? If oil is no longer produced in Purbeck in fifty years time, then the 'Landscape on Loan' will revert to its former heathland habitats. The industrial archaeology of the heathlands will no doubt be a point of visitor interest, with Norden being a key centre for study of the history of mineral exploitation on Purbeck's heath.

Farm landscapes have changed greatly from the nineteenth century as mechanisation revolutionised farming. Yet change in the future is difficult to forecast. Will climatic change bring a selection of new crops to a warmer Purbeck? Who could have forecast the vast new acreages of maize that have appeared in the second half of the twentieth century? Purbeck's one vineyard at Harman's Cross may well be the first of several others. Will the Army finally give up the Lulworth Ranges and farm enterprises spread more widely into the western vale? Will the Army stay and the ecology of western Purbeck still have its undoubted protection?

Village landscapes will change, although probably in the slow fashion of the last fifty years. Villages will expand but slowly, and infill new housing will remain the route to providing new accommodation. Affordable housing schemes, like those in Corfe Castle will become more urgent. Purbeck will continue to attract the retired and second home seekers will still search estate agents'windows for a rural retreat. Old housing in Purbeck will need modernisation and improvements, but not at any cost. Most villages have already lost their general stores and sometimes their Post Office. Corfe is likely to remain the most vibrant of the villages: others will slumber on into the twenty-first century and retain their essential Purbeck charm. Will there be a by-pass for Corfe Castle, or will the environmental difficulties render it impossible without irreparable damage to the landscape? Traffic into Purbeck will have increased unless the road-pricing that now seems inevitable will have had the desired effect on reducing the number of journeys that people make into the area? In fifty years time Purbeck should have a railway connected to the national network, and this could ease the traffic problems in some villages.

Affordable housing, Corfe Castle.

How will Purbeck's townscapes have changed? In the centre relatively little change will probably have taken place. Electronic shopping on the Internet may have changed our shopping habits, but not enough for a difference in the shopping landscape to be noticeable. Supermarkets have made inroads into the viability of individual traders over the last fifty years, although many of the latter have survived. Parking will be an even greater problem in the two town centres, particularly in Swanage in the summer; park and ride schemes are inevitable. Wareham may well expand to the north: will the new residential areas at Holton Heath have materialised? Will Treves' fears for Swanage be more fully realised? Will there be many more 'unlovely backs of unashamed homes'? Purbeck at the beginning of the twenty-first century has landscapes that are still full of charm and rural character. They reflect a physical background of rock, relief and soil of infinite variety, and a micro-climate that many say is distinct. Thousands of years of human occupance have shaped the landscape of town, village, farm, field and hamlet in the peninsula that is a very special part of Dorset. Purbeck's landscapes charm with their infinite variety. A new visitor standing on the summit of Creech Barrow will be welcomed by physical and human landscapes that have retained those intrinsic attractions that appeared at the beginning of this book. In a changed Britain it is likely that they will have even greater appeal.

Sunset, Worbarrow Bay.